"Does my name mean anything to you?"

Did it ever! Ivory's thoughts were hysterical. He was only the man she had come to Amsterdam to meet—the head of the Alexander Corporation himself.

Oh, Ivory, she couldn't help thinking, when you make a blunder, you certainly make a blunder!

Her assignment had been simple: fly to Amsterdam, deliver some important papers to Lawson Alexander and fly home the next day.

But instead of executing her mission with a minimum amount of fuss, she had wandered late into the wrong hotel room. Unintroduced and unnoticed, she had spent the whole night asleep in one bed, while this man had slept in the other!

The Icicle Heart

by

JESSICA STEELE

Harlequin Books

TORONTO • LONDON • NEW YORK • AMSTERDAM
SYDNEY • HAMBURG • PARIS • STOCKHOLM

Original hardcover edition published 1979
by Mills & Boon Limited

ISBN 0-373-02297-2

Harlequin edition published in November 1979

CHAPTER ONE

'WHO the hell are you?'

The harsh sound of a deeply timbred voice brought Ivory up from the depths of sleep. Not believing she had heard the rude, abruptly spoken words, she lay for a moment on the plateau between sleep and full wakefulness. She couldn't remember having dreamt—she had been so tired when she'd flopped exhausted into her hotel bed last night she could barely remember anything, and assumed the words that had sounded so clear must have been the tail end of a dream, the rest of which must have faded into obscurity.

'Would you mind telling me what the hell you're doing in *my* room?'

The voice came again, causing her to come instantly wide awake. She had her back to the speaker, so all he could have seen was the back of her honey-blonde hair as she snuggled amid the covers. But the shock of hearing the sound of a masculine voice in the privacy of her bedroom had her whirling round in the direction of the voice, her violet eyes growing wide with horror and the beginnings of fear as they took in the all male figure propped up in the bed opposite her.

'Who . . . ?' she began. But her voice came out in a squeaky whisper as her mind tried to cope in its rudely awakened state with the dark-haired, dark-eyed, bare-chested individual whose glance was raking her every feature and taking in what he could discern of her shape from beneath the bedclothes as well.

Belatedly aware that her shoulders were fully exposed to his unrelenting gaze, Ivory tugged the sheet up around her. 'W-would you mind telling me what you think you're doing in m-my room?' she managed, finding her voice and glad to note the squeak had left it, while her eyes flicked hastily to the phone as she tried to assess her chances of summoning help if the man in the other bed turned out to be some raving maniac.

She watched him closely, alerting her limbs to be ready for action if he took it into his head to make a dive at her. Though to be honest he didn't look at all as though he had any such intention as he lay there indolently surveying her. His eyes had narrowed at her question, she saw, and she wanted to swallow to relieve the fear that was drying her throat.

'Drop the pretence,' she was told coldly, her question ignored, 'and just tell me what your little game is. Whatever it is I can promise you it isn't going to work.'

Sure now that she was in the company of a raving madman, Ivory was forced to swallow on the hard knot of fear that gripped her. 'I don't know what you mean . . .' she began, only to have her words chopped off mid-air, as with an irritable movement the man sat up, causing her to shrink back a few inches as his well muscled torso moved in her direction.

'Cut it out,' she was told icily. 'I didn't come down with the last shower of rain. If it's blackmail you have in mind—forget it.'

'Blackmail!' Ivory gasped. 'I don't know what you're talking about.'

He gave her an exasperated look as though not believing her, but undecided what to do with her. And as some of her fears subsided as realisation came that he seemed more concerned with putting the blame on to her for being perfectly legally in her own room, when he must know he was the interloper, some of her deserted spirit returned.

'I haven't any idea what you're talking about, and I think you know it,' she said, an unfamiliar ice entering her usually warm-sounding voice. 'A-and I would be pleased, as *you* are the intruder into *my* room, if you would go—just get up and leave *now*.'

Again she felt herself come under the close scrutiny of his dark look, and thought in that look he was summing her up, was weighing the few things he could possibly have learned about her in the last five minutes against the look of her, with only her head visible, her hair mussed up and her face free of make-up. She then saw he must have drawn enough from his deliberations of her to have his conclusions neatly docketed, for the next words he said were spoken easily, the harshness gone. But his words shocked her more than anything he had said previously.

'I was thinking of getting up anyway,' he said, moving his position slightly, his hand ready to flip back the covers. 'I sleep in the raw, but I'm sure . . .'

Ivory's squeak of alarm had his hand immobile when she'd thought he was going to accompany his words with action, and she could do nothing about the embarrassed colour that flooded up beneath her skin.

'Good God!' seemed to be dragged from him as he witnessed her heightened colour. 'The maiden blushes—or is maiden a dirty word nowadays?'

Since she wasn't about to tell him that was exactly what she was, Ivory peeped out at him from beneath her lashes, ready to close her eyes quickly if he made any sort of move to get out of bed.

'I . . . I think I'd better get up first,' she said, knowing that at that moment the importance of impressing upon him that the room was hers was less urgent than the need to get some clothes on. She would feel better equipped to deal with him once she was dressed.

'As you like.' His voice was unconcerned, but she could see his eyes were still on her.

'Would you mind . . .' she began, hoping she wouldn't have to ask him outright to turn the other way.

'I don't mind a bit,' he said, being deliberately obtuse, she thought. Then as if he'd suddenly just caught on, 'Oh, do you sleep in the raw too?'

Ivory glared at him. She was at his mercy—she knew it, and he damn well knew it too. She was wearing a perfectly respectable nightie, but she wasn't in the habit of flitting round in her night attire in front of any man, known or unknown.

Since it must be obvious to him that she wasn't going to move until he had the decency to look the other way, she lay tense waiting for his next action. It was a relief when she saw he had tired of the game he was playing.

'You know,' he said almost conversationally, 'nice girls don't make a habit of dossing down on any spare bed they happen to find.' And without waiting to see what she made of that, he turned his back towards her.

Ivory didn't waste any time. In a flash she was out of bed, snatching up her overnight case from beside the bed where she had deposited it late last night, and was inside the adjoining bathroom the door slammed shut and bolted. Only then did she realise how much she was trembling.

For some seconds she stood trying to control her shaking limbs, then stared into the mirror at the face that looked back at her. Her flush of colour had disappeared, her cheeks looked unusually pale and her eyes were saucer-wide.

The thought came to her that he might come banging on the door at any moment, and in trembling haste she un-latched her case, a sigh of relief escaping her as she noted that the papers she had brought with her from England in such a rush last night didn't look in any way tampered with. Then taking out the change of underclothing she had brought with her, and the jeans and sweater she had put in for no known reason when she hadn't thought she'd be wearing them, she raced to get washed and dressed.

As she'd hoped, her nerves had quietened down once she was dressed, though in her rush, she had left her handbag in the other room and could have done with the confidence a touch of lipstick would have given her. Still, that couldn't be helped, and as she had been too tired last night to unpack the few things she had brought with her, at least her hair-brush was still in her case, so she could do something about her tangle of hair.

About to leave the bathroom, she put her ear to the door. She could hear nothing, but didn't know if that denoted that her unexpected night visitor was still in the other room or had taken it into his head to wander into the sitting room of the suite. It was certain he had no business being in the hotel; any normal person would have flicked on the light switch when getting ready for bed. Her mind took off for a few moments as she pictured him stealthily creeping about getting undressed, while all the time she had lain unsus-pectingly asleep. What would have happened if he'd elected to sleep in the bed she had chosen, heaven only knew, she thought with hair-raising horror. But thank the lord he had not; as it was she was left with the very serious dilemma of whether to report her intruder to the hotel management or not.

The trouble was she had never been to Amsterdam before,

wouldn't be here now if there hadn't been such a flap going on in the office back in London and if aptly nicknamed Dizzy Williams hadn't forgotten to renew her passport. She only hoped Mr Alexander wouldn't be too put out that she'd arrived instead of Dizzy.

There was no further time to wonder what Lawson Alexander would have to say when he found that a girl unknown to him had arrived instead of the expected Dizzy, for on the point of screwing up her courage to leave the bathroom, Ivory distinctly heard the sound of voices coming from the other side of the door. Listening hard, she couldn't make out a word that was being said, and almost laughed to herself, but not quite, as the thought came to her they could be speaking in double Dutch, before she realised the voices must be speaking in Dutch. She heard the slight chink of crockery and putting two and two together realised early morning tea must have arrived.

That caused her to swallow once more. True, she hadn't thought to order early morning tea—had been too tired to think of that luxury—but what on earth would the maid think, expecting to find a Miss Ivory Dutton in possession and finding that broad-shouldered individual instead?

Hearing a door close, she listened for a further few seconds before thinking it safe to come out of the bathroom. Why she hadn't come out while the maid was there and told her the other occupant was an intruder she couldn't think, other than that she had a feeling she would be more embarrassed than he would. For even undressed he had an air of savoir-faire about him.

He wasn't in the bedroom when she peeped her head out, but the door leading to the sitting room, she saw, was wide open. Straightening her shoulders and taking a calming breath, she went through and stopped at the door to see he was calmly sitting before a small table—just as if he had every right to be there—and was coolly drinking a cup of what looked like coffee, and reading a morning paper. He was dressed, she saw, and from the smoothness of his chin had taken the opportunity of her absence to shave himself, though she couldn't for the moment see where he could have plugged in his electric razor.

'Coffee?' he offered, making no move to pour her any.

Ivory ignored him, went to check the time, then realised her watch was still on the bedside table where she had left it. As she wandered back into the sitting room strapping her watch to her wrist, she saw it was only seven o'clock. Not quite believing it, for it seemed as though this whole nightmare had been going on for hours, she lifted her wrist to her ear. Her watch was still going—that gave her a couple of hours before she met Mr Lawson Alexander at nine. She had a couple of hours in which to put this traumatic experience behind her before she handed over the papers she had brought with her from London—once that was done, she could fly back straightaway.

Lifting her eyes, she saw the man was watching her and hurriedly looked away. The very casual, unconcerned air he had about him caused her further disquiet about what to do about him. Then knowing she was way out of her depth, and with everything within her crying out for this matter to be settled with the minimum amount of fuss—Lawson Alexander wouldn't like any publicity gained from this, she felt sure, her imagination seeing bold headlines in the paper Alexander's representative finds man in her room', she advanced further into the room, her eyes looking anywhere but at him.

'There are two cups here!' she exclaimed in surprise, her glance falling on to the tray in front of him.

'I didn't know how you'd feel about sharing my cup as well as my room,' he said calmly. 'I rang down for coffee for two.'

'You . . .' Words failed her. The gall of the man! The absolute, utter . . . She tried again. 'You know perfectly well this is my suite,' she stated coldly, suddenly longing for a cup of coffee to relieve her parched throat. 'You're dressed now, so why don't you go away? I . . . I won't say anything to anybody. If you can't afford to pay for a room . . . well, I'm sorry, but you really can't just—stroll into a hotel and take up any bed that happens to be empty, you know.'

The man didn't move. Ivory wondered if she really expected him to. For all he was dressed casually in sweater and slacks, they looked expensive enough to indicate that he could well afford to pay for his overnight board at any of the most exclusive hotels—and she knew the one the Alexander Corporation had set her up in didn't come cheaply.

'I wonder what you propose to do if I don't go,' he said slowly, and instead of looking worried at her attempt to turn him out, looked amused instead.

Ivory knew she was floundering. This man, whoever he was, seemed to be openly ridiculing her, and short of calling the hotel management there seemed very little she could do about it. On the other hand, she wasn't prepared to let him sit there and laugh at her efforts to shift him.

'I'm afraid you leave me no alternative but to call the hotel manager,' she told him severely, walking towards a telephone she had noticed sitting on a desk against the wall. Reaching her hand for the instrument she saw with puzzlement that there were some papers on the desk, but before she could get her thoughts together about what they were doing there, his voice arrested her. And it wasn't the voice he had used a few moments before. There was none of the lightness or humour in it when he spoke, but a coldness that told her he had been going along with her so far, but now her threat had aroused hostility in him. There was authority in his voice too, that had her turning sharply to look at him.

'You should have attempted to telephone for help the instant you awakened, Miss Dutton,' his voice cut into her, the use of her name, the fact that he somehow knew who she was causing her to forget she had been about to ring for assistance and have him thrown out. 'Good God, woman, anything could have happened to you.'

'Y-you know my name,' she stammered, wondering wildly if he was some member of an industrial spy gang out to get the papers she had brought with her—though not being sure they would be of interest to any firm other than the Alexander Corporation.

'You left your bag when you went to get dressed,' he told her briefly.

'You've been in my handbag?' she questioned, not quite believing he could calmly tell her so, while her mind became convinced he was definitely an industrial spy.

'Naturally,' he said, as if he couldn't see anything wrong in what he had done. Then testily, as though he didn't think it necessary to explain any of his actions, 'It had crossed my mind you might have some notion to try some form of blackmail, and I wanted to know with whom I was dealing—your passport tells me you're Miss Ivory Dutton.'

Ivory looked at the telephone, then looked back at him. He had stood up and come over to her, and topped her by a good six inches for all she was five foot seven in her stockinged feet. He had an athletic look to him that went well with his dark looks, and the sheer authority emanating from him had her wondering what she did now.

'This is my suite,' she almost whispered, as though by

establishing that fact she would gain charge of the situation.

'Correction,' he said, his eyes not moving from her face. 'The rooms are mine.'

'Yours?' She was feeling lost suddenly.

'There has obviously been some mix-up,' he said, seeming to unbend slightly from his cold attitude at the bewilderment in her face. 'Suppose you tell me what makes you think you have a right in here.'

At last it looked as though he was prepared to be reasonable, she thought, some of her tension lifting. 'The man on reception gave me the key,' she told him, and knowing she must be in the right rooms unless the receptionist had made a mistake, went on, 'It was late when I arrived last night.' She wasn't going to admit to being so weary she could hardly keep her eyes open—this man facing her would take it she had made the mistake in her tiredness and she knew she hadn't. 'I'm here on business,' she added, and felt quite proud that the Alexander Corporation had thought well enough of her after only six months' service that they entrusted her with this mission—though she'd take jolly good care they didn't learn about this episode! 'I asked at the desk for the man I'm here to meet and they seemed to know he was expecting me, because straight away they gave me my key and said to go up.'

A barely perceptive movement from the man facing her had her looking fully at him. In other circumstances she would have thought humour was having a battle with the frost in him, but his face was humourless as he dropped out smoothly:

'I take it Dizzy couldn't make it?'

Ivory sank down on to a chair that fortunately was near at hand. 'Y-you know Dizzy?' was drawn breathlessly from her. And as the fact that of course he must do to mention

Dizzy's name dawned on her, a tingle of alarm shot through her while the dreadful thought came, Oh, no, he can't be—causing her to ask jerkily, 'Who . . . who are you?' She thought the silence would go on forever as she waited for his answer, and wanted to disappear beneath the floorboards when his answer finally came.

'Does the name Lawson Alexander mean anything to you?'

Did it? she thought helplessly—he was only the man she had flown to Amsterdam to meet, that was all. The head of the Alexander Corporation—the big noise who had had everyone rushing around in circles when his message had been received that he wanted a certain set of papers from his safe together with some calculations that meant a full day's work being cut to four hours in order that the information he wanted could be flown out to him in time for a meeting at ten o'clock the next morning. She didn't want to believe he was the man she had been sent to meet, and had to force herself to drag out her next question.

'Are you Mr Alexander?'

She knew he was before that slight nod of acknowledgement with his head. And she had been hoping no one in London would know about this episode! Oh, Ivory, she couldn't help thinking, when you make a blunder, you certainly make a blunder! Far from executing her mission with the minimum amount of fuss, she had flown in last night, very much in awe of meeting the great Lawson Alexander for the first time—and the first time she had met him had been across the bedspace of the twin beds in what could only be, she was forced to concede now, *his* hotel room. She had in fact—unintroduced—spent the whole night asleep in one bed, while the man who had the power to make heads roll at Alexander's had slept in the other.

Whether he guessed anything of what was going through her mind she had no idea, but his voice was less cutting as he went and poured her a cup of coffee and handed it to her.

'It's not as hot as it might be, but you look as though you could do with something to drink,' he told her.

Ivory took the coffee from him, managed to find sufficient strength in her vocal cords to utter a polite, 'Thank you,' and was glad of the brief respite drinking her coffee allowed for her to get her thoughts into some kind of order.

'I can't understand it,' she said, when the silence in the room became overpowering, for it seemed that having discovered she was one of his employees, Lawson Alexander was in no hurry to give her the dressing down she was expecting. 'I'm sure I couldn't have made a mistake.'

'Don't worry at it, girl,' she was told shortly. 'There's no damage done—I don't expect I'm the first man with whom you've shared a room.'

Ivory felt a spurt of anger shoot through her at his cold summing up of her morals. One guess was sufficient for her to know women were no stranger to his bedroom—but it annoyed her that he could think she was fair game. Ignoring his remark, she chose to discuss the reason for her being here in the first place.

'I have the papers you asked for in my case. My instructions were to hand them to you at nine this morning, but you may as well have them now.'

He made no comment while she bent over her suitcase and extracted the all-important papers that had seemed so urgent yesterday in London, for all he gave them no more than a cursory glance as she handed them to him.

'I take it Dizzy Williams couldn't come?'

Dizzy Williams was a sort of floating secretary-cum-courier with the Corporation, a job she thoroughly enjoyed.

It was said she had a very clever brain, but her tendency to overlook smaller details had earned her the nickname Dizzy. It seemed to Ivory a bit like telling tales to tell Lawson Alexander that Dizzy had forgotten to renew her passport— so seeing he was becoming impatient for an answer, she gave him a monosyllabic, 'No,' and found herself favoured with a sharp look from his dark eyes at her short answer. It was as if he knew she was trying to cover up for the other girl.

'She's not ill, is she?'

'N-no, she was quite well when I left,' Ivory was forced to confess as his eyes held hers in a straight no-nonsense look.

'I expect she didn't find out until the last minute that her passport was out of date,' he said levelly, with such brilliant deduction that Ivory could only stare at him.

'How on earth did you know that . . . ?' she gasped, unwittingly confirming his surmise, while thinking if his mind always worked so quickly it was no wonder he was head of the Alexander Corporation at his age. Rumour had it he was anywhere between thirty and forty; she rather thought he looked to be somewhere in the middle.

'Dizzy didn't get her nickname without good reason,' he told her in an offhand way. 'All the same, she's a damn good courier.'

'You mean she wouldn't have found her way to the wrong bedroom,' Ivory couldn't help challenging him, and couldn't help wondering either what nickname would be bandied about the office for her if any of this leaked out when she got back.

'Don't let it throw you,' he told her. 'I thought London would be sending Dizzy, and that being so I instructed reception to send her up to my room as soon as she arrived. Dizzy would have known to have left the papers and gone to her own room. I expect you told them at the desk that you were here to see me?'

She nodded. That was exactly what she had done—gone straight to the reception desk, said, 'I'm from the Alexander Corporation—I'm here to meet Mr Lawson Alexander', and after being handed one set of keys had been too tired to hang around to see if there was anything else. After all, her instructions were to call on him the following morning. She'd just assumed the key she had been given was the key to the room that had been reserved for her. That the key opened the door of a suite hadn't registered properly in her tiredness.

Her reflections were cut short by Lawson Alexander breaking in, 'I haven't seen you before. Have you been with the Corporation long?'

'Six months.'

She hadn't seen him before either, but had heard about him. It was said he was a man who worked hard, but was not averse to playing with equal intensity.

'You work as Dizzy's assistant?'

'Oh, no, I'm in the statistics department—on the secretarial side. There was a . . .' She halted briefly, then thought, Why not let him know the furore his telephone call had caused? She had an idea her chances of promotion were nil after the mess she'd made of this trip anyway. 'There was a bit of a flap on yesterday after your call, so everybody who could be spared was called in—Mr Fletcher,' she went on, mentioning her immediate boss, 'was away at our Manchester office yesterday, so I was free to give a hand. We'd almost finished and people had started to go home when Dizzy discovered her passport wanted renewing.'

'So you were seconded to fill in for her?'

'Yes.'

That brief word didn't cover the half of it. But that was all she chose to tell him—she didn't think he'd be interested in hearing how she'd piped up unthinkingly that her own passport was valid; it pleased her that the thought of her unused passport no longer hurt as much as it had done six months ago. Dizzy had looked at her, then to the man who had organised everything that day, and said, 'Why not?' and before she knew it, she was being packed off home to the flat she shared with Mandy, was stuffing a few things into an overnight case and racing back to the office. Even so, with all the rushing about that had gone on that day, it had gone eight before she had finally made it to the airport and was aboard the plane that would take her to Schiphol airport; from there she had made her way to Amsterdam. By the time she reached the hotel it had gone midnight, and the events of the day—no time for meal breaks—had caught up with her. Small wonder she had fallen asleep as soon as her head had touched the pillow.

Glancing now at her watch she saw it still wasn't quite half past seven. She had never been out of England before, and wondered what she did now. It was for sure Lawson Alexander wouldn't want her cluttering up his hotel suite for very much longer—the best thing would be to take a taxi to the airport and wait there for a plane which would take her home. Lawson Alexander, she saw, had gone to stand, half turned from her, staring out of the window, his pensive expression telling her he wasn't seeing the view, but that his mind was on some other matter—probably deep in thought about making his next million, she thought with unaccustomed cynicism; he had that effect on her.

'Is there any message you want me to take back to London?' she asked, feeling suddenly uncomfortable as he

turned away from the window and came to fix her with
another of his dark glances.

'Can you type?'

It wasn't the answer she was expecting, but she kept her
face straight, showing none of her surprise at his unexpected
question.

'I told you I'm a secretary,' she reminded him.

He gave her a look which she took to mean that didn't
signify anything these days, then said, 'Good—you won't be
going back today.'

Ivory couldn't cover her start of surprise this time. 'Mr
Fletcher will be expecting me this afternoon,' she felt bound
to protest. They had their own work schedules in the statistics department. Mr Fletcher would go spare if she didn't
get back to do at least some of his letters.

Lawson Alexander gave her a look that needed very little
interpretation. She guessed rightly Mr Fletcher wouldn't
have the nerve to argue against any decision he made. He
ignored her protest as she should have known he would
when she voiced it.

'I have a meeting at ten—working through lunch I should
be back here some time this afternoon. I'll have a typewriter sent up—you can work in here.'

Ivory found herself accepting without further argument
that since a major problem had blown up with some business
in Amsterdam, and since she was now on the spot, she had
been co-opted to work for Lawson Alexander. But she
couldn't help the spark he irritatingly aroused in her that
caused her not to want to make things too easy for him.

'What do I do meantime?' she asked edgily. She hadn't
any commitments at home, but it irked her that he hadn't
bothered to ask if it was convenient from her personal point
of view for her to stay.

'You can start by going to the room that's been reserved for you,' he told her shortly, letting her know he thought she had taken up far too much of his time already. Tight-lipped, she looked back at him, and if she hadn't already got the message, he added, 'Since you'll be staying here another night, maybe two or three, I would rather you did that straight away—I prefer to choose for myself who shares my room with me.'

Ivory almost gasped at the sheer effrontery of the man. That he could calmly imagine . . .! Her anger cut off further thought, and as if her heels were on fire, she snatched up her case, muttering a mild but heartfelt swearword as the clasp came undone and the petticoat she had worn yesterday fell out. Hurriedly she stuffed the petticoat back again, then snapping her case shut and with her handbag over her arm she stormed to the door. Her colour was high, but this time she knew it was more from temper at what he had just said than from embarrassment at him having seen her underwear. The insinuation that she might even be willing to *voluntarily* share his room caused flags of temper to flush her cheeks. At the door, she turned and looking straight into enigmatic dark brown eyes, any thought of counting up to ten leaving her as she saw the sardonic look that came over his face.

'You'd be lucky,' she said tightly, and without waiting for any reply he might care to make, she stormed out.

On her way down in the lift to the reception area, her temper left her as more immediate concerns took priority. How on earth was she going to look whoever was on duty in the eye when they saw she had come to claim the key to her room not from the door that led in from the street, but from inside the hotel itself? Fresh colour surged through her face as the thought hit her that the receptionist would know where she had spent the night.

As the lift doors opened she toyed with the idea of leaving her case behind a nearby pillar, and as she approached the pillar she was sorely tempted to do just that and make believe she had just come in from the street after taking an early morning stroll. Until it dawned on her that she hadn't even checked in yet and, what was more to the point, she had no idea what the number of her room was.

She was in sight of the reception desk before she had fully made up her mind what action she was going to take. Then the indecision was taken from her, for the receptionist had spotted her and to her relief, as she neared the desk, she heard the girl ask in perfect English:

'Miss Dutton?'

'Er—yes,' Ivory admitted, while her brain accepted the fact that the receptionist could only have known who she was if she had been tipped off that she would be calling at the reception area. Lawson Alexander must have phoned down, she realised, as she went up to the girl.

'Your key, Miss Dutton—I must apologise for the mix-up last night when you arrived,' the girl said pleasantly, seeming not to notice the overnight case Ivory was clutching in her by now moist hand. 'I am glad we were able to get you inside your room with the pass key, but now the proper key has been found.' She handed Ivory the key with its metal tag, which Ivory accepted with as much of a smile as she could muster.

'Thank you,' she managed, then realising the other girl was waiting politely with seemingly no intention of asking her to sign in, she said, 'Thank you,' again, and retraced her steps back to the lift.

CHAPTER TWO

HAVING gained the room where she would be spending that night, and according to Lawson Alexander, possibly the next two or three nights, Ivory slumped down into a small armchair trying to sort out everything that had gone on since she had opened her eyes that morning to the sound of that harsh voice asking, 'Who the hell are you?'

At the end of ten minutes she had come to one very clear conclusion—Lawson Alexander might be her boss, might be clear-thinking, dynamic and all the other things that were said about him, but one thing was for sure, she disliked him more than any other man she had ever met. True, there had been no need for him to phone down to reception and make things easier for her, but that didn't make her dislike him any the less.

Without the slightest doubt the time spent working with him in Amsterdam was not going to be any picnic, and without the aid of a crystal ball she knew that when she returned to England her visit to Amsterdam would be something she wouldn't want to remember.

Thinking of the next two or three days in his company brought her involuntarily to her feet. Having thought she would only be staying over night, all she had with her was the suit she had hastily changed into when she had dashed home from the office to pack, a change of underwear and the jeans and sweater she now stood up in.

Two hours later, having breakfasted—while keeping a careful eye open in case her employer should take it into his

head to come into the dining room at the same time, it would
be bad enough working for him, she saw no reason why she
should have to suffer him at mealtimes too—she had returned to her room, rinsed through the underthings she had
worn when travelling yesterday and decided that since
Lawson Alexander would not be requiring her services until
some time in the afternoon, she might just as well take the
opportunity of exploring Amsterdam.

Seeing it was a different receptionist on duty gave her
courage to go up to the desk and ask what places of interest
she could suggest she visit. Ivory soon realised there were
a great number of attractions Amsterdam had to offer, and
settled for a visit to the Rijksmuseum.

'Can you tell me how I get there?' she asked the girl, who
was proving herself more than helpful.

Ivory found the Dutch people she met more than willing
to assist her and she was aided with buying her ticket to
board the tram. More than one voice was ready to tell her
when she had reached her required destination, being quite
uninhibited when it came to trying out their English.

'Thank you—thank you very much,' she smiled as she
stepped lightly off the tram.

There was much more to see in the museum than there
was time for, she realised, but she thoroughly enjoyed her
morning as she drifted for the most part enraptured by the
sculptures and paintings on display. She would have loved to
have visited the library as books were a special love of hers,
but she knew if she were to do that she would lose all sense
of time, and she mustn't be late getting back to the hotel.

Pangs of hunger gnawed at her as lunch time came around,
and she made her way to the restaurant she had seen when
she had entered the building. She had very little Dutch
currency left, she realised as she paid for her meal, and

although it had seemed ample when the finance department had handed the money over yesterday, it had only been meant to cover her overnight expenses. Still, she decided, no good would come of worrying over it. If she had all her meals in the hotel, she probably wouldn't need to spend anything else.

Looking at her watch she saw it had gone two. If she didn't want to let herself in for Lawson Alexander's undoubted wrath, she'd better get back to the hotel. She was, she conceded, being paid by him, but she wished her first trip abroad had been to meet someone more pleasant.

The same receptionist greeted her when she returned, asking, 'Did you have a pleasant time?' Ivory told her she had, and couldn't help but think how nice everybody had been to her that day—everybody, that was, except *him*.

Not knowing what time she could expect to hear from the head of the Alexander Corporation, she spent some minutes rinsing her face and applying fresh make-up. Undecided whether or not to change into the suit she had travelled in, she surveyed her slender figure in the mirror—jeans and sweater weren't quite the uniform for the efficient secretary she was about to prove she was, she thought, which decided the matter for her. Half way towards the wardrobe, her intention to take out her suit, she was halted by the ringing of the telephone.

Not sure whether to answer with her room number or her name, she said neither and instead said, 'Hello,' and felt her flesh tingle as she recognised Lawson Alexander's voice.

'Come to my suite,' he ordered in the cool tones she was learning to associate with him. 'Come now,' he added, and hung up.

That 'Come now', meant exactly what it said, Ivory realised, turning her back on her wardrobe. There would be no time now to change—though she wasn't going to hurry. Dropping the key of her room inside her bag, she went at a moderate pace to obey his summons.

The floor his suite was on was above hers, and ignoring the lift she climbed the stairs and soon enough was lightly tapping on his door. She had just sufficient time to take a deep breath, then heard the immediate command, 'Come in.'

Lawson Alexander was dressed formally in a dark business suit—and looked very different from the casually attired man she had left so angrily earlier in the day.

'Sit over there.' He indicated a typing chair Ivory hadn't noticed before that was placed before the desk. The desk now housed a typewriter, and she managed to bite down the question that rose to her lips of where had he managed to obtain it. A small thing like having a typewriter and typing chair installed in his suite would present no problem to a man of his ability.

He didn't start work straight away as she had supposed he would, but looked her over carefully, his eyes coolly taking in the fact that she was still dressed as she had been when last he had seen her.

'Have you been out?' he enquired, coming to stand a foot or so away from her shoulder.

Ivory was forced to turn her head upwards to look at him. It was a long way to look up and she could do nothing about the warm look in her eyes as she remembered some of the wonderful paintings she had seen.

'I went to the Rijksmuseum,' she told him quietly.

'I can see you were impressed—I take it you're an art lover.'

'I think I fall into the "I know what I like" category,' she answered, and was glad when he didn't pursue the subject any further but began to give her notes to take down.

He began slowly at first until he was sure she was coping —she had an idea he wasn't the type to want to repeat himself. Then when he saw she was managing to keep up with him without any trouble, he speeded up his dictation until her fingers were fairly flying across the paper.

After some time he broke off. If he felt any admiration that she had been able to keep up with him, she realised he wasn't going to show it. But she couldn't help but feel an inner pride in her own achievement. She knew she was good, had had the best speeds in her class at secretarial college— but this was the first time she had taken shorthand from anyone as high-powered as the man now resting the backs of his thighs against the corner of the desk.

'If you can transcribe and type as well as you take shorthand, I should think you're wasted in Statistics,' he said, to her surprise.

She was unable to help the glow of pleasure that he had— in a roundabout way—complimented her after all, but was careful not to show how much his praise had pleased her.

'I don't think you'll have anything to complain of,' she told him as evenly as she could manage. 'Mr Fletcher has never found reason to complain of my work.'

She almost blushed as the words left her lips because it sounded so very conceited and she hadn't meant it that way at all. From his look she could tell her words hadn't impressed him—he was probably used to a much higher standard than Mr Fletcher anyway, she thought, and wished she'd remained silent.

Knowing it futile to try and explain she wasn't being bigheaded, she pulled the typewriter towards her and began opening a box of carbon paper resting on the desk.

'There's a good few hours' work there,' he said—an

understatement, Ivory thought, but said nothing. 'I suggest you work from now until six, then you can go to your room and rest for a while—then you'd better come to dinner with me. You can finish off any typing left over tomorrow.'

Shock at his cool suggestion—no, order—so calmly given, that she dine with him, his not even giving her the chance to refuse, was the uppermost emotion she was feeling as she turned round on her stool.

'If it's all the same with you,' she told him primly, 'I would much prefer to dine on my own.' She wondered afterwards at her own temerity in declining his invitation, for it was obvious from his stony expression that it was the last thing he expected to hear.

'What's the matter?' he asked after a few moments silence. 'Afraid the boy-friend will object?' and not giving her time to answer, for all the words rushed to her lips, 'I can assure you, Miss Dutton I'm not at all interested in you *that* way.' Then really letting rip into her, obviously peeved for she guessed very few women had ever turned down an invitation from him, 'Honest to God, you women!' he exploded. 'Just because a man has caught a glimpse of your naked shoulders, you think he can't wait to get his hands on you!'

Ivory forced herself to stay calm. She didn't think now was the time to tell him that from the way he had been studying her before she had covered herself up, he had caught more than a glimpse.

'It . . . It's not that at all,' she protested, trying to keep her composure. 'I never for a moment thought what you're thinking.'

'Why then be so coy about a perfectly ordinary dinner?' he asked, his tone anything but reasonable. 'I won't tell the boy-friend if you won't.'

'I haven't got a boy-friend,' she said shortly, and only

just managed to stop herself from saying 'now'. She'd put Michael Stephens out of her thoughts six months ago—or told herself she had, though it still upset her when she thought of the way they had parted.

'Not for the want of offers, I'd say,' he said, his cold tone taking any flattery out of his words. 'So, if you aren't afraid of boy-friend trouble when you get home—and you aren't thinking I shall turn out to be the big bad wolf—why do you want to eat alone? Are you a loner or something?'

Ivory sought for some way to tell him she felt uncomfortable in his company—she had never purposely hurt anyone in her life—and though she doubted her refusal to have dinner with him would affect him in any way at all, for all the fuss he was making about it, she realised there was no way she could tell him without making it sound blunt.

'I haven't anything to wear,' she came up with at last in a flash of inspiration. It was the truth, she hadn't, and although that wasn't the reason she didn't want to dine with him, she didn't think he would think much of taking her to dinner in the grey suit she had travelled in. 'I thought I should be going back this morning,' she felt bound to explain, 'so I have only the suit I travelled in and what I stand up in.'

He didn't argue the point, but gave her a shrewd look as if suspecting her of fishing for something. Innocently, Ivory returned his look, then felt herself go red all over when his look changed to one of cynicism and he straightway pushed his hand inside his pocket, withdrawing his wallet. Still with the cynical look on his face, he pushed a handful of notes in her direction.

'In that case,' he declared coolly, 'you'd better nip out and buy yourself something, hadn't you?'

Without her being aware of what she was doing, Ivory's

hands instinctively went behind her back in a childish gesture of refusal. 'No, thank you,' she said quickly, realising now he thought she had been angling for him to buy her something to wear. She felt quite sick at the thought and knew she would wear her suit or jeans until they dropped off her before she would accept his money. Lawson Alexander's indrawn breath of impatience at the game he thought she was playing stiffened her resolve. 'I'm not in the habit of allowing any man to pay for my clothes, and . . . and I feel offended that you thought that was what I was asking.'

Her words were quietly spoken, and with dignity. She didn't expect him to believe her. She guessed he was no stranger to settling the accounts of his mistress of the moment, but she was, as she had told him, deeply offended that he could think what he had so obviously thought.

A lengthy silence fell between them. She knew he was looking at her trying to weigh her up. Whether he believed her or not was immaterial to her just then, she wouldn't back down and he had no power to make her.

It was Lawson Alexander who was the first to speak. And at his change of tone, the cynicism dropping away from him, a hint of warmth entering his cool tones for the first time, she realised by the very fact she had not raised her voice but had delivered her refusal in quiet dignified tones that he was half way to believing her.

'I've offended you, Ivory,' he said, using her christian name for the first time, 'and that was not my intention. But as your employer I feel a responsibility to you. You're in a country foreign to you, and although the people here are very friendly, they speak a different language. I don't think I would be doing my job properly if after making you stay in Holland I then abandoned you to sit alone in the lounge or in your room tonight. For that reason I would be pleased if you would dine with me.' Ivory felt herself weakening as he turned on the charm that must have felled many a lady friend, and steeled herself against him. 'As for my paying for your clothes—you can forget any ideas you have that I shall be footing the bill. You will feel more at ease this evening in a dress, I'm sure,' he added, giving her a fair indication that he had in no way accepted that she wasn't going to dine with him. 'But since you're in Amsterdam on company business, the finance department will naturally expect you to draw expenses on your return.'

Ivory just had to look at him then. He sounded so sincere. Her eyes met his dark look and she saw his mouth had turned up at one corner in what could have been an encouraging smile. She looked away from him. She didn't want to be charmed by him. The trouble was, never having been on an all-expenses trip before, she had no way of knowing if a new dress was part and parcel of the procedure.

'Why can't I have dinner in my room?' she felt bound to protest.

'Because I would be falling down on my job in management if I allowed you to do so,' he came back sharply.

Ivory knew Alexander's took pride in taking care of their staff, but couldn't help wondering if Lawson Alexander wasn't taking that caring a shade too far. She knew she was on the way to being beaten, but found it went against the grain to give in easily.

Then again her powers of decision were being taken away from her, for she felt his cool clasp on her wrist and found the bundle of notes thrust into her hand after all.

'If you don't look sharp you'll find the shops will be closed,' he was telling her matter-of-factly. And as she just stood there as if turned to stone, her hand clutching the money he had given her, he added, 'Be sure to get receipts for everything you buy—the finance department are sticklers for receipts.'

Fifteen minutes later Ivory was walking smartly into the dress department of one of Amsterdam's many stores. She was only vaguely aware of having been pushed out of Lawson Alexander's sitting room. She had little recollection of leaving the hotel, and only really came to as a sales lady came forward to help her.

Being more or less stock size she was easy to fit, and after a fifteen-minute search came across a dress in dull pink that showed her figure off nicely, having a fitted bodice and flaring out over the hips. It had short flared sleeves, and the only problem she could see with it was that the deep shoulder line was cut away so far that she would just have to buy a bra to go with it—that or risk giving Lawson Alexander a view of her shoulder straps every time he looked her way at dinner. Pride in her appearance would not allow that to happen, so after handing over some of the notes he had given her, though having very little idea of their value, she asked the English-speaking assistant for a receipt and then made her way to the lingerie department. The object of her hasty dash to the shops completed, she made her way back to the hotel.

She debated taking her purchases back to her room, then glancing at her watch saw it was now five-thirty. Would he expect her to do half an hour's typing? She had no idea, but since she had some change from the money he had given her, she decided to take it along to him and see what happened from there.

'Get what you wanted?' he asked when he answered her knock and stood back to allow her into his room.

'Yes, thank you.' Ivory handed him the change and saw him slip it into his pocket without bothering to count it.

'I've got the receipts here,' she said, handing those to him as well. 'I . . . I needed to get—something else,' she found herself stammering, and railed against being too embarrassed in this day and age to say the word 'bra' to this wordly-wise man. She knew she was blushing as he took the receipts from her and flicked his eyes over them, guessing, since he had spoken Dutch earlier that morning, that he also had no trouble reading it.

He looked up before her colour had subsided, and she saw his puzzled glance for a second before the reason for her blush dawned on him. She waited, half expecting him to make some comment on her high colour, but he remained silent for a second or two, and she had the oddest feeling he was really seeing her for the first time.

'If it will save you further embarrassment I can claim for these items on my expenses form,' he suggested, making it sound the most natural thing in the world—matter-of-fact, but leaving the decision to her.

Ivory had already decided to repay him the money she had spent as soon as she arrived home, but the way he suggested would save her having to make contact with him again.

'Would you mind?' she asked, knowing she would rather pay for everything herself than have Finance query her need to buy a bra while she was away on business. She wouldn't have thought that in his position Lawson Alexander would have to fill in an expenses claim—though he was probably the sort who kept all facts and figures neatly on order.

He didn't answer her question, but slipped the receipts into his pocket, then glanced at his watch. 'It's not worth your starting on the typing now—we'll call it a day. I'll see you at eight in the lounge bar, all right?'

Ivory couldn't help but be pleased with the image that

gazed back at her from the full-length mirror of the ward-robe later. Without being conceited she knew her appearance would not let Lawson Alexander down that evening. She was still suffering from mixed feelings about him. Upper-most was the thought that while she was in Amsterdam she was forced more or less to do as he requested. But since in the six months she had worked for the Alexander Corpora-tion she had heard plenty about him but had never so much as clapped eyes on him, she hoped that once back in Eng-land, back working in her usual environment, she might never have to set eyes on him again.

Ever since her love affair—if one could call it that—with Michael had finished, she had been at pains to become self-reliant. She was off men, and had received many invitations out, but never again did she want to grow close to anyone as she had been to Michael. Though according to Michael the converse of that was true of their relationship. It had been his reason for wanting to end their engagement—the fact that for a couple who were on the verge of getting married the closeness of the relationship was not as close as he would have liked.

She shrugged thoughts of Michael away as she gathered up her bag to go to meet her employer. She'd thought the days had gone when every avenue of thought always came back to thoughts of Michael.

Lawson Alexander left his seat by the bar as she entered. While Ivory wasn't looking forward to the next hour or so she was being forced to spend with him, she couldn't help but feel flattered that the tall, good-looking man coming over to her, completely oblivious to the one or two dis-creetly veiled glances in his direction from several of the women in the room, appeared not interested in anybody but her. Oh, she knew there was nothing personal in his invitation, but a glow she hadn't expected to feel washed over her as he came to stand in front of her.

'For a women who must have spent less than half an hour in purchasing a gown, may I say you couldn't have done better if you'd spent all day.'

Ivory acknowledged his compliment with a small smile, and when he asked what she would like to drink asked for a medium dry sherry. Doubting they had anything in common, she wondered what on earth they would find to talk about, and suspected since they had no common ground except the Alexander Corporation they would spend the time through dinner talking shop.

But to her surprise he seemed disinclined to talk business, save to mention that he had been the other side of the world when things had started buzzing in Amsterdam.

'You had to drop everything and come to Holland?' she asked, cutting into a delicious steak, only then realising the importance of his business in Amsterdam since it must be top priority for the head of the Corporation to drop everything to come and sort out the problem.

'As I expect so did you,' he answered, making light of the speed with which he must have moved to nip the near-disaster in the bud. 'You're very young,' he went on thoughtfully, his eyes looking directly into her limpid violet ones. 'I trust your parents didn't mind your coming over on such short notice?'

He hadn't shown any interest in whether it had been convenient for her to leave her home in such a hurry before, she thought, and she wasn't sure he was particularly interested now or just making polite conversation. Still, since he was making the effort, she'd better say something—that or spend the remainder of the meal in dumb silence.

'I'm twenty-one,' she told him, putting down her knife

and fork, having finished her main course and ready for a breather before the sweet trolley arrived. He was obviously waiting for her to add more to that, and she was half annoyed with herself when she found herself volunteering the information, 'My mother and stepfather live in Luton—I came to live in London six months ago.'

'You get on well with your stepfather?' he asked, as if surmising that was the reason she had left home.

She thought his question a shade personal, and answered quickly, 'My stepfather's a love—I couldn't ask for better.' She should have known with his analytical mind that his questions wouldn't stop there.

'What made you come to London? You don't seem to me to be the type to want to try her wings in the big bad city.'

Since he knew nothing at all about her, and she guessed he had seldom entertained anyone of her type to dinner before, she thought he was assuming rather a lot.

'I don't think you have any idea what type of person I am,' she said shortly. She barely knew herself, and was glad the waiter arrived at that moment with the gateau she had selected. She waited until Lawson Alexander was ready to cut into his cheese and biscuits and thinking she had cleverly put an end to any further speculations he might have about her, picked up her fork and spoon and began to eat.

'You live in London?' he asked, letting her know he wasn't finished with her yet, for all her previously short answer.

'I share a flat with a girl friend.' It had been a pure stroke of luck that Mandy had been looking for someone to share at about the same time Ivory had decided she had to leave Luton.

'You've contacted her, of course, and told her you won't be home for a day or two?'

'Mandy's away herself at the moment doing a spot of supply teaching.'

'So there's no one in England who's likely to worry about your absence?'

Ivory was beginning to feel irritated by his flow of questions. She thought he was taking the Alexander reputation for watching out for staff and their families just a little too far.

'There's no one likely to be in the least worried if they don't hear from me for a few days,' she told him, holding tightly on to her temper. 'My mother is a very common-sense sort of person—if she rings the flat and gets no reply she'll ring the office and find out where I am. Mandy won't be back until Friday night—and there won't be any boy-friends holding their fingers on my doorbell!'

'Ah,' he said, and if she didn't know better, she could have sworn there was a wealth of satisfaction in that 'Ah', as if at last he had got to the whole point of their conversation. She shrugged the thought away; he was a sophisticated sort of man, he wouldn't be interested in the love life of one of the secretaries his company happened to employ.

The coffee arrived, and having refused his offer of a liqueur, she concentrated on spooning brown sugar into her coffee while at the same time endeavouring to get rid of the feeling the man opposite her unerringly managed to arouse.

'Would I be right,' he voiced casually, his glance leaving the cheroot he had just lighted to come to rest on her, 'in thinking there haven't been any boy-friends for the last six months?'

It had been a mistake to try and appear as casual as he. It had been a mistake to nonchalantly lift her cup to her lips to take a sip in a nothing-you-can-say-can-jolt-me fashion, for his question, so unsuspected, and so absolutely bang on target, had the effect of almost making her choke. How she controlled it she never afterwards knew, but by a supreme effort she was able to swallow, though she was unable to risk another sip. Hoping he hadn't noticed how her hand was shaking in her agitation, she returned her cup to its saucer.

It was while she was fumbling around in her mind for an answer that would cut him down to size that she became aware that someone had come to stand at their table. And as her glance flicked upwards to see who it was and what they wanted, she heard the slightly husky voice of a beautiful red-haired girl, six or seven years older than herself, breathing, 'Lawson darling, I didn't know you were in Amsterdam. What a lovely surprise!'

It was no surprise to Ivory that the red-headed girl ignored her; her attention was all for Lawson—she had no interest at all in his dinner companion.

Lawson rose to his feet saying courteously it was an unexpected pleasure to see her. 'Let me introduce you to Miss Dutton,' he said with grave charm. 'Ivory, meet Miss Sheba Nightingale.'

Since Sheba Nightingale showed no intention of wanting to shake hands, Ivory smiled acknowledging the introduction. Her smile wasn't returned, and she was left wondering why, since the other girl was now positively beaming at Lawson. Then with a slight feeling of shock, she suddenly realised that Sheba Nightingale was jealous that she was dining with him, and could have laughed out loud at the absurdity of such an emotion in regard to her and Lawson Alexander—Why, if she hadn't arrived when she had, they would probably by now be in the middle of a full-scale row as she would have followed through her intention of telling him to mind his own business and not question her about her boy-friends.

They had been exchanging pleasantries for a moment or two when she heard Sheba say she had dined and was meeting friends later. But when she made no move to go and join them and Lawson remained standing, Ivory realised he wouldn't reseat himself until she went away.

'Won't you join us for coffee?' she heard him ask politely. She wasn't in the least surprised when the beautifully turned out redhead accepted.

Knowing Lawson was just about to summon up another chair, she got to her feet. She had finished her meal and now that Sheba Nightingale had joined them, she felt surplus to requirements anyway.

'You can have my seat,' she said, ignoring the hard look Lawson was giving her and smiling directly into the hard blue eyes of the new arrival. And so that the girl should be under no illusions about her relationship with him, 'I'll report for duty in the morning, Mr Alexander.'

Without waiting to see whether he intended to stop her or not, she sailed out of the dining room with her head held high. There was no pleasing some people, she thought. Lawson had looked anything but pleased at being left alone with the luscious-looking redhead.

On reaching her room Ivory couldn't help but give a sigh of satisfaction over her action. She hadn't wanted to dine with him in the first place, and had taken exception to his astute question over her lack of boy-friends. And she felt now, in the privacy of her bedroom, that Sheba Nightingale's arrival had been most timely. A small laugh escaped her as she stepped out of her shoes. She was feeling on top of the world—she knew she could hardly put the light-hearted feeling down to the stimulus of the company she had just left. Though she had to own that sharpening her wits against Lawson Alexander had brought her more to life than she had been just lately. She hoped she was still feeling as bright when she had to face him again in the morning.

When a short sharp knock sounded on her door some twenty minutes later, some of her good spirits deserted her. Without opening the door she knew who would be on the other side, and she swallowed quickly while she debated the wisdom of answering. Knowing him, though, he would have left nothing to chance and could easily have enquired at reception if she was in—or seen for himself that her key wasn't on the rack. Quickly she slid her feet into her shoes. Even with her two and a half inch heels she wouldn't match his length, but the added height gave her more confidence to open the door.

One glance at his face was sufficient to tell her he wasn't very pleased with her. She faced him, her heart going like a trip-hammer, though she was determined she wasn't afraid of him for all his importance.

'Did I forget something?' she asked, making her voice even when in reality she wanted to slam the door on the face that took on fury at the insolence of her question.

'Only your manners,' he told her tightly. 'Don't you ever dare run out on me again!'

The controlled way in which he spoke each word told her it would be better if she stayed quiet, but something in her she didn't know she possessed refused to let her stay quiet.

'I'm sorry,' she said, trying to look sorry, but not succeeding very well. 'I didn't mean to offend you.' He had offended her that day and thought nothing of it, so why *should* she be sorry? 'I rather thought you and Miss Nightingale might have something personal to discuss—I didn't want to be in the way.'

'When I want your help in running my personal life I'll ask for it,' he told her sourly. 'Until then while you're in my employ and on company business, you'll do as I tell you. You'll be dining with me again tomorrow night—run out on me then and I'll have you dismissed.'

Ivory was left staring at him open-mouthed. He had made no move to enter her room—she knew she couldn't have stopped him had that been his intention. She was learning enough about him to know he always got his own way. But to talk of having her dismissed purely because she had walked out without finishing her coffee was a bit much.

Satisfied that she had no answer to that, some of the fury seemed to leave him, and in cold tones he went on to tell her the arrangements for the next day.

'I have a meeting at nine in the morning—I'll drop the key of my room in to you on my way out. You should have sufficient typing to keep you busy until I get back.' Not bothering to say goodnight, he left her staring at his straight broad-shouldered back as he strode away from her.

CHAPTER THREE

IVORY didn't sleep very well that night; she had too much on her mind. What she should have done, she reasoned as she tossed and turned in her bed, was to have told Lawson Alexander what he could do with his job.

On reflection, though, she thought, as dawn broke through and with it common sense, she was glad she had not taken that course of action. She had settled down very well in the short time she had been at Alexander's. She liked the people she worked with and if the work was a little boring at times, she managed to make it hold her attention enough not to have her mind wandering off with thoughts of Michael. And that had been the whole object of her leaving Luton and all the associations it held for her.

A solid rap on her door brought her up from the depths of sleep. Her eyes were not fully adjusted to the daylight filtering through her window as she leaned over and picked up her watch from the bedside table. Just gone half past eight. *Half past eight*! She was not conscious of further thought as she leapt out of bed. The knock on her door came again as she reached it.

Mindless of her tousled hair, unaware of the pink flush of sleep still on her cheeks, she opened the door a few inches, her eyes coming rapidly awake as she saw a business-suited Lawson Alexander standing there. What he had been going to say she had no idea, but she thought it was the last thing he meant to say as he paused and took in the look of her.

'Twenty-one, did you say?' he said softly, a glint of

humour showing through. 'You look more more like sixteen this morning.'

'I—er—overslept,' she mumbled, feeling strangely tongue-tied. She wished her brain had woken up with the rest of her when she'd opened her eyes, for she could find nothing to say to him. Then she saw there was no need to say anything, for suddenly he became all businesslike, extending a hand to her which forced her to stretch her bare arm to take the key he was offering.

'You'd better take this as well,' he said, pushing some Dutch money into her hands. 'I expect Finance only gave you sufficient to cover overnight expenses—I'll claim for it with my expenses.'

Her mind was still arguing the fact she didn't want to take his money, while common sense was telling her the few guilders she had in her purse were not sufficient to cover any emergency that might arise. While another part of her was disbelieving that the head of Alexander's would have to fill in an expense sheet when he returned to London.

Instinctively she made a move to thrust the money back at him, but since he had a briefcase in one hand and had raised his other hand to examine his wrist watch, there was nothing she could do but take the money unless she was to reveal herself to him still in her nightie.

He caught her instinctive movement, seemed to know the reason she wouldn't open the door any further, and she could have sworn a self-satisfied grin was about to break through before he smothered it.

'I should be back some time around three. You have a lot to get through. I've left you some notes I'd like typing as well as the typing you already have to do, but don't break your neck—and be sure to take a proper lunch hour. If you can't read my writing it will have to wait until I come back.'

There was a hint there that his writing might be pretty abominable, she thought. 'I'm sure I shall manage,' she told him. 'My stepfather is a doctor and I manage to read his scrawl all right.'

She couldn't help that a mischievous grin broke from her then. There was nothing she could do to hold it back at the impudence Lawson must think she had to intimate that his writing was a scrawl before she'd even seen it. She looked up and saw his dark eyes watching her. Instantly her smile vanished, for his look was considering as his eyes rested on her lips before returning to look into her eyes.

'I can see you feel cheeky first thing in the morning,' was all he said as he left her.

Ivory hurried round her room after she had closed the door. She had no idea what time they finished serving breakfast and decided to be more organised tomorrow morning. She would leave word at the desk to give her an alarm call.

Wearing the grey suit with the pink blouse she had travelled in, she returned from a hasty breakfast and went straight along to Lawson's room. She'd better get on—one never knew, he might return early and she didn't fancy banging away on the typewriter with him there.

His writing, to her surprise, was better than she had expected. And being used to seeing her stepfather's only just decipherable hieroglyphics she was soon able to pick up that when Lawson wrote anything ending in *ing* it was always written as a line with a 'g' on the end as though he was impatient to get on to the next word.

Working solidly through the morning, she looked at her watch only when her stomach told her it would be grateful for anything she sent down. Half past one. She checked the pile of neatly typed documents, surveyed the amount she still had left to do and decided her stomach would have to wait. She would like something to drink, though. Unused to hotel life—not sure of any of the do's or don'ts—she wondered what Lawson would do if he wanted a drink.

Feeling a little like royalty, she picked up the phone and asked would it be possible to have coffee sent up, and was delightfully pleased at how easy it was when the voice at the other end said pleasantly, 'Certainly, madam,' and within minutes a tray of coffee arrived. Ivory took ten minutes off to drink her coffee, then feeling rested, once more set to work.

Engrossed in what she was doing, she didn't hear Lawson coming along the corridor two hours later, and jumped startled when the door opened and he came in.

'How's it going?' he asked, dropping his briefcase down on the floor while his other hand went up to undo the top button of his shirt and loosen his tie.

Ivory took her eyes away from the manly column of his throat, finding his easy gesture faintly disturbing. 'I've almost finished,' she told him, turning back to her type-writer.

'Have you?' he queried, slightly disbelieving, she thought, as he came over to examine the completed pile to one side of the desk. He picked up the top typewritten sheet.

If he's examining it for mistakes he won't find any, Ivory thought. She took a pride in her work and because it was for him, had taken extra care to keep her work smudge free and accurate.

'You couldn't have had any lunch,' he accused, replacing the paper he had taken up.

Trust him to know that! 'I wanted to get on.' She hoped he wasn't going to ask why. The last thing she was going to confess was that she had been endeavouring to get the work completed so she could be out of his room when he returned.

She relaxed when he let the subject drop, but only to tense again when she heard him on the telephone ordering sandwiches to be sent up and a tray of tea.

Knowing it was too late to argue the point, his order had been given now, she applied herself to the typewriter, not stopping when a knock came at the door—he had ordered the sandwiches, he could jolly well take delivery of them!

She felt him come to stand and look over her shoulder, but refused to let her fingers cease in their activity. She only hoped he would go away before her fingers fumbled. She'd hate to give him the satisfaction of seeing her reach for her eraser. He walked away as she came to the bottom of the page and Ivory gave an inward sigh of relief that the sheet had been completed without her having to rub out.

'Pack that in now and have a bite to eat.'

She turned round on her chair, about to argue that she'd nearly finished, then she saw there were enough sandwiches for two and he was already tucking in.

'I worked through my lunch hour too,' he said, and there was such a definite gleam of humour in his eyes now that she had to smile, especially since he had made a point of instructing her to take a proper lunch hour.

He left it to her to pour the tea, and she found for the first time as they demolished the sandwiches between them that there was no animosity in the air. We're both too tired to fight, I expect, she mused, for she noticed his briefcase was open and bulging with papers which told their own story of the work he himself had put in.

Never having expected to feel relaxed in his company, she was half way through her second cup of tea when it came to her that he was just as human as she was. There were lines of tiredness around his eyes, telling her he had spent a hard morning, and she judged he must have worked well into the night to get his own notes written as well as leave her the handwritten work he had done.

When he told her she needn't do any more that day, that she could finish off in the morning, her instinct was to protest. She had nearly finished anyway—but then she paused to wonder if perhaps he wouldn't go into the bedroom, stretch out on the bed and rest for an hour or so if she went. There would be no chance of that while she was banging away on the typewriter.

'Are you sure?' she asked. Then greatly daring, 'What about you—I . . . mean, are you going to do any more today?' She held her breath, knowing she had just ruined the ease that had been between them. It just wasn't the thing to do to intimate that the head of the Alexander Corporation had done enough for the day.

But he didn't take exception to her question as she had thought, but slid his eyes in the direction of his briefcase. 'I just might,' he said, and smiled directly at her for the first time.

He's got lovely teeth, she thought, and I like the way his whole face lights up when he smiles—it made him look nearer thirty. Aware she was staring, Ivory flicked her eyes down to the cup and saucer she was holding. Embarrassed suddenly to be caught staring at him as though hypnotised, she stood up placing her cup back on the tray.

'I . . . I think perhaps I will finish off tomorrow,' she said, wanting to be away from the room and his oddly disturbing presence. He had said last night that she would be dining with him again tonight, but he hadn't mentioned it today, and since he had almost flattened her with his fury when he had told her she would be dining with him, she didn't like to be the one to bring it up.

Her eyes flicked over the desk making sure she had left everything tidy. Then having ascertained he could have no complaint, the completed documents all neatly in order, she made to leave the room.

'Why not go and have a blow of fresh air?' His voice stopped her before she reached the door. 'We're not going out until eight—you have plenty of time.'

'I might have a wander round the shops,' she told him, more to get herself out of the room than from any concrete plan.

'Don't be afraid to spend your money. Dizzy always has a bonus after these trips—I'm sure you'll get the same, and I can always pay you your bonus here if you run short.'

She hadn't known about the bonus, and had thought she would be returning the money he had given her intact, but ... She looked down at the front of her blouse; it had looked so crisp when she'd put it on fresh on Monday, and she had a thing about wearing a blouse two days running without it being washed through.

'I could do with a few things,' she admitted, feeling bound to explain lest he thought she was being greedy. 'I didn't bring very much with me.'

His look said he understood perfectly, and at his understanding, she smiled. He seemed to like her smile, even though he didn't return it. 'Off you go, then.' His voice was now offhand. You couldn't get more offhand, Ivory thought as she went along to her own room with his casual, 'See you later,' echoing in her ears.

It didn't take her long to reach the shops. Her mind as she went, though, was not on the purchases she would make, but on the man she had left not half an hour ago. He'd said they weren't going out until eight, his only reference today that last night he had ordered her to dine with him—and stay with him until he told her she could go; that or be dismissed. She chose not to think about his cold anger of last night, but wondered instead where they would be going, since he had intimated that they wouldn't be eating in the hotel.

She realised as she made her way into one of the big stores that really she had no axe to grind. If, as Lawson had said, she was due for a bonus at the end of this trip, then it surely followed that she wasn't expected to keep the normal nine-to-five office hours. Not that she was a clock-watcher in any case—it was just that it rankled to be *told* she was dining with him, her right to choose with whom she ate taken away from her.

Within a very few minutes she had found her way to the lingerie department, and there she purchased a couple of pairs of briefs, a bra and some tights. She had no idea when she would be going home, but with these items and those she had brought with her she could rinse out the things she had worn that day and they should see her through until she got home. Next she bought a white blouse, the pink one she had on couldn't possibly stand another wear without being washed—she could keep the white one to travel home in. It would have to be jeans again tomorrow, though, un-businesslike as they were. Still, there was only Lawson there to see them and he seemed to understand the position. Then on leaving the department store she saw a top that would do to go with her jeans, and bought that as well.

Arriving back at the hotel, she still had plenty of time in which to get ready. So after washing out a few more items, she lay in the bath and had a luxurious soak, feeling the strain of sitting at her typewriter for almost seven hours leaving her. She was dressed and ready when Lawson's knock sounded on her door. She would have liked to have been able to ring the changes by wearing a different dress from the pink one she had worn last night, but conceded that it still looked as good now as it had done then.

'Ready?' This evening, in contrast to the lounge suit he had worn last night, Lawson was wearing a dinner jacket, and Ivory was struck by how well it became him. 'Have you got a coat you can put on—it will be chilly later on.'

'I've only the jacket to my suit,' she told him, not thinking he would want to take her out wearing that when she suspected the women he usually escorted were dripping in mink.

'Go and get it,' he ordered her. 'It might hurt your eyes, but it'll save you catching pneumonia.'

There was nothing for it, she saw, but to do as he wanted, for he looked as though he had no intention of moving until she had her jacket about her shoulders. 'You'd better come in,' she invited, and left him standing inside her door while she opened the door of her wardrobe.

She felt uncomfortable that he had full view of the contents of her wardrobe. Any inventory he would care to make wouldn't take him very long, she thought, for all the wardrobe contained was a pair of jeans and the grey suit she had worn earlier that day. She was grateful he didn't make any comment as he helped her into her jacket.

Lawson had left the door open when he'd come into her room, and now stepped back to allow her to precede him into the corridor outside. It was as they were going down in the lift that he told her they were not dining alone.

'I've arranged to meet an old friend of mine,' he told her. 'I was at school with Jan and couldn't visit Amsterdam without looking him up. I think you'll like him.'

It was on the tip of her tongue to ask why it was necessary for her to join the party, but she kept her silence. She was past wondering what motivated Lawson Alexander's actions. Though she had a feeling if this Jan person and her employer were going to reminisce on their misspent youth, she would be decidedly in the way.

Having decided in advance that she was sure, contrary to Lawson's prediction, she wasn't going to like his friend, she found herself taking almost instantly to the slim Dutchman when they joined him in a quiet hotel. He came over to them as soon as they entered the lounge, greeting Lawson with the warmth of old friends, then turning to be introduced to her.

'Lawson told me he had an assistant with him this trip, but he never told me his assistant was female and a salve for tired eyes,' he told her with so much charm that Ivory could do none other than let her smile break through.

'If you want to powder your nose, the room is through there,' Lawson broke in before she could think up a reply to his friend's compliment.

Ivory looked up quickly at Lawson's sharp interruption to Jan's greeting, saw there was no warmth in his eyes, which caused her to wonder briefly what she'd done wrong now, before she tossed the thought aside as it dawned on her that Lawson was clearly telling her she could leave her jacket with the cloakroom attendant if she wished. She should have been grateful to him for reminding her she still had on the jacket of her suit, she realised, but as she went along to the powder room she felt anything but grateful. Lawson had dropped the amiable air he had adopted with her as soon as they had met his friend. If he was regretting having brought her, he shouldn't have forced her to come in the first place, she fumed.

Contrary to her expectations, as she left the powder room, that she was in for a rotten evening, she found as each delicious course followed another that she was really enjoying herself. She knew she owed most of her thanks for this to Jan Hansen, for Lawson Alexander wasn't saying very much to her—but the Dutchman more than made up for him.

'This is your first time in Holland?' he asked her, when she had just finished chuckling over something he had said.

'This is my first time anywhere abroad,' she told him, feeling at ease with the man, who was about the same height as herself, and warming to his ready smile. As the words left her lips she thought they sounded very naïve and wished them back as soon as she'd said them.

Looking away from Jan, she glanced in Lawson's direction and came up against his stony stare. She flicked her glance away; something had soured him, but she couldn't think of a thing she had done wrong.

'My usual assistant in these matters found at the last moment that her passport was invalid,' Lawson told Jan, the friendship of years excusing any bluntness in his tone.

'It was lucky you did have a valid passport, then, Ivory,' Jan told her. Then he asked her a question that had her searching around in her mind for an answer. 'You must have been preparing for a trip abroad to have your passport ready?'

'I . . . er . . .' Nothing would have made her tell the two men waiting for her answer the truth, that she had applied for a passport more than six months ago when she had thought she would be spending her honeymoon abroad. 'I . . .' She was floundering and hoping it wasn't showing when unexpectedly Lawson came to her aid.

'Ivory's foresight was my gain—I couldn't have managed without her.'

If Jan noticed his question had gone unanswered, he did not press her further, and then the waiter arrived with a delicious lemon sorbet, and conversation became general, though Ivory was still wondering at Lawson's timely intervention, more so because he had said he couldn't have managed without her. She let her mind play with this as the two men talked over a point that didn't require her to add anything. And she realised her flight to Amsterdam had been very important to Lawson because without the facts and figures she had brought with her, he would have had to attend his meetings with less than half the information—something she knew he would be loath to do.

After their meal they lingered for some time in the bar, Lawson and Jan unable to help now and then from catching up on news of mutual friends. But courteously Lawson saw she was not left out and when he consulted his watch—a sign, she saw, that they were about to leave—she was ready to collect her jacket, thinking that for all she was aware Lawson wasn't very happy with her, she had enjoyed her evening in Jan's company.

The three of them went to the door of the lounge together, Ivory leaving the two men briefly to return with her jacket over her arm. She had no intention of wearing it, but her employer's sharp though quietly spoken order of, 'Put it on,' had her shrugging into it with Jan's assistance.

As the three of them said their goodbyes, Jan mentioned that he would be visiting London in a few weeks' time. Then turning to Ivory he asked, 'Are you free tomorrow evening?'

It was the unexpectedness of his question that had her not knowing what to answer. She had sensed through the evening that Jan liked her as she had taken to him. But since she was under the threat of dismissal if she disobeyed any of Lawson's orders, she looked at him to tell her whether she was free tomorrow night or not.

Intercepting the look, Jan followed his invitation by

speaking directly to Lawson. 'You can't be expecting Ivory to work tomorrow night, my old friend,' he said, his ready smile showing through. 'For old times' sake take pity on a poor bachelor, and let her have the night off.'

'For the sake of our friendship, I would that I could,' Lawson told him, a glimmer of amusement showing through as he said with some deliberation. 'But you see, *old friend*, Ivory and I are travelling home after my meeting tomorrow.'

Ivory's eyes flew wide as she turned to look at her employer. It was the first she'd heard they were going home tomorrow. She looked from Lawson to Jan, and couldn't help wondering what went on between these two, for she was receiving a distinct impression that they were scoring points off each other.

It was Jan who gave in, and he turned to her with a look on his face that said he was disappointed he would not be seeing her tomorrow. 'Perhaps I might be lucky enough to see you on my visit to England?'

'I should like that,' Ivory told him, suddenly happy that for the first time in six months she was ready to go out with company other than female. Perhaps I'm part way to being cured of Michael, the thought popped unbidden into her head, and though she was nowhere near yet ready to contemplate falling in love again, a beaming smile accompanied her words at her discovery that she was at last beginning to come to life again.

The taxi ride back to their hotel was made in complete and utter silence. Ivory for her part didn't care if she never spoke to Lawson Alexander again. As far as she was concerned she had done nothing wrong, and whatever was bugging him she felt he could sort out for himself; she wasn't going to make conversation just to have him jump down her throat!

Good manners decreed that she waited for him while he

paid off the taxi, and when he courteously held the door leading to the hotel open for her to go through, she unlocked her throat sufficiently to mutter a polite, 'Thank you.' She waited a little way away from him as he collected both their keys, and walked beside him to the lift.

It was Lawson who broke the silence between them as the lift ascended. 'I take it you are about to break your six months' rule?'

He could only be referring to the fact she had told him she hadn't any boy-friends and his astute surmise was based on the fact that there hadn't been any since she left Luton six months ago.

'Have you any objection?' she asked, hoping to sound sarcastic, but as the words left her icily, realised sarcasm wasn't her forte. Only then did it cross her mind to wonder if he thought she had taken advantage of his introduction and been over-friendly with Jan. She turned abruptly as they stepped out of the lift on her floor, giving him the full benefit of wide violet eyes. 'You think I shouldn't have been so friendly with Jan, don't you?' she accused, feeling let down by the thought that Lawson was a class snob. Though why it should bother her what sort of man he was, she couldn't think, for she had very little liking for him at all. 'You think I should have told him I wouldn't see him when he came to London, don't you?' she went on, feeling the heat of anger come to swamp over her let down feeling. She was every bit as good as they were!

'My dear Miss Dutton, you can do what the hell you like,' Lawson told her coldly. Then after a brief pause as he watched the sparks of anger light up her truly lovely eyes, 'After all,' he said, finding all the sarcasm she had found herself incapable of, 'it's not every day a girl can pull a diamond millionaire.'

'I didn't know . . .' Ivory began, before the insinuation he was implying hit her. 'Why, you . . . you . . . snob!' was the worst thing she could think of to say that was within her code of utterances. And not waiting to see what he made of that, she stormed off along the corridor to her room. Either that or stay where she was and give him the hefty kick on his shins he had been asking for ever since he had introduced her to Jan earlier in the evening.

Too late she reached her door, to remember he had the key to her room. She stood outside her room fuming quietly. She wouldn't go back and ask him for it—she just wouldn't! She'd go and get the pass key sooner.

'Allow me,' said a voice behind her shoulder.

So he had followed her. Unspeaking, Ivory stood to one side as he inserted the key in the lock, but when she would have pushed past him and gone into her room totally ignoring him, she found he still had his hand on the handle. Since she wanted no contact with him, whatsoever, she was forced to wait until such time as he chose to let the handle go.

'So you think I'm a snob, do you?' he asked chillingly, pinning her with his dark gaze. The ice in his voice told her as clearly as any action of his could have done that he didn't take kindly to the name she had called him. 'Since I'm in the same financial bracket as my very good friend's, perhaps I'd better prove that I believe we are all created equal.'

Ivory didn't like at all the way he was looking at her. She saw the challenge, the determination in his look, but was completely unprepared for the way his hands snaked out and pulled her towards him. There was a brief moment when their eyes locked, and she gasped in horror at the realisation of what he was about to do. Then he had half carried her with him inside her room and as she heard the door click behind him, his hard unrelenting mouth came down on hers.

She struggled wildly in his arms, but he refused to let her go until he had his satisfaction. But as he at last took his mouth away from hers, she saw there was little satisfaction to be witnessed in his direct look.

Ivory took a sharp step backwards. Now that Lawson had released her she realised how badly she was trembling. Her legs felt weak and she would have given anything to sit down, but she was too wary of his next move to let him see her weakness.

'Good God, don't look like that, girl!' Lawson barked at her, witnessing from the pallor of her cheeks and the look in her eyes how shaken she was. 'I'm not going to rape you!' Then as she didn't speak, but just stood there eyeing him warily, 'Oh hell, it wasn't my intention to frighten you— just . . .'

'Teach me a lesson,' she finished for him huskily. 'So now I know,' she said, glad to hear her voice was getting stronger. 'Never again should I call the head of the Alexander Corporation a snob. You teach your lessons the hard way, Mr Alexander, but I'll remember in future.'

It was incidental that after tomorrow there would be no future contact between them. After tomorrow she would go back to being a secretary in Statistics, and she doubted that their paths would ever cross again.

Not having taken her eyes off him, she saw a tight-lipped expression come over his face, and her own face showed a stubborn line.

'I can see it's useless trying to talk to you now,' he said tightly.

'That's right, it is. Would you mind leaving my room—I take it school is now over?'

Lawson made a movement at her words which gave her a clear impression he would like to have caught hold of her and shaken her until her teeth rattled, but whatever he felt like doing he managed to restrain himself.

'Report to my room at nine sharp,' he said. Then taking

his eyes off her for the first time since he had let her go, 'And don't lose any sleep over the fact you've just been kissed for the first time in six months. If you weren't so frozen up inside—who knows, we both might have enjoyed it.' With that parting remark he left her.

Ivory felt the relief of tears spurt to her eyes once she was alone. She hated him—God, how she hated him! She brushed a hand across her cheek and it came away wet. At last able to begin to relax, she sat on the edge of her bed and howled her eyes out. How dared he kiss her like that—who did he think he was? And to say she was frozen up inside— how could he have known? Surely he hadn't expected her to respond to his insulting kiss?

A few tears trickled through long after she had undressed and got into bed. She tried to pull herself together. She hadn't cried like this since Michael had told her he didn't think they should get married after all.

She thought for some time about Michael. Michael, who had been so wonderful to be with—thoughts about her ex-fiancé brought with them thoughts of the last time she had seen him. He had been nothing like the Michael she had fallen in love with then, as he told her coldly that the honeymoon they had planned would never come to fruition. And all because he felt they were physically unsuited. It sounded cold now thinking about it in the solitude of her room, but what Michael had been saying boiled down to the fact that since she couldn't bring herself to sleep with him before their marriage, he doubted she had the warmth in her to make that side of their marriage a success. He wouldn't listen when she had tried to tell him she had no worries on that score. Ivory was sure once they were married their love would flower into beautiful culmination. It was just that her mother, having been widowed when she had been a baby, had been extra aware of her responsibilities to her daughter. She had given her an extremely sheltered upbringing, impressing on her early in life a very strict moral code, and in consequence Ivory had always been rather reserved when it came to getting emotionally involved with anyone.

She sighed as she turned over in her bed. Since Michael she had not had any other boy-friends. Oh, there had been invitations enough, but as Lawson Alexander had found out without too much trouble, she felt herself frozen over when her engagement ended. She tried to picture Michael's face, but the only image that presented itself was that of her employer glowering at her as he told her, 'I'm not going to rape you'.

CHAPTER FOUR

IT was with some trepidation that Ivory knocked on Lawson Alexander's door at two minutes to nine the following morning. Ever since she had awakened she had been building herself up against this moment, and now she heard his voice fully in command call, 'Come in,' all the courage she had screwed together deserted her.

It required quite an effort to turn the handle of his door and go in—she could hardly remember what she'd said to him last night, but recalled that she'd felt quite fiery, so she could have said anything in temper. The room was empty, though the bedroom door was ajar, and this gave her a few more seconds in which to summon up her control before Lawson came and stood in the doorway.

His scrutiny of her was slow and deliberate and she found herself locked by his gaze, unable to move. Her earlier intention to enter his room, toss him a cool 'Good morning' and present him with her back as she went over to the desk faltered and disappeared.

'You've been crying?' he said, his tone accusing.

Damn, she thought she'd managed to disguise that fact. Probably she had done to all but someone as sharp as him. 'My tears weren't all on account of you,' she said without thinking, and could have bitten her tongue out, for that was the last thing she wanted him to know.

His eyes narrowed slightly as he closed the bedroom door and came further into the room. 'It would seem my kissing you triggered off far more than I meant it to,' he said to himself, then clearly, 'I take it thoughts of your lost love were the cause of some of your tears?'

He was so clever, she thought mutinously. She'd never met anyone like him for putting two and two together and coming up with the right answer. Defiantly she turned on him.

'Yes,' she said, her ire rising. 'Since you know so much—yes, I was crying about . . .' Her voice fizzled out with her burst of temper before she could bring herself to mention Michael's name.

'A wasted exercise, surely. If you still want the fellow so badly, why throw him over in the first place?'

It shook her for a moment that Lawson could think she had been the one to throw Michael over. She was tempted not to answer, but a mixture of honesty and compulsion as his narrow-eyed gaze held hers forced the confession out of her.

'Your guesswork is at fault. I was the one to be thrown over.'

'Indeed?' he said slowly. The word, though brief, held a world of meaning—as if her statement had surprised him. 'What's wrong with the fellow?' he asked.

'There's nothing wrong with Michael,' she came back quickly in his defence, saying his name without realising she had said it. Then, unable to bear the force of Lawson's scrutiny any longer, she turned away from him and went to stand over by the desk.

'You're intimating that there's something wrong with you,' he said shrewdly addressing her back, and as she refused to answer, 'What, I wonder?' His tone had her thinking he meant to find out. Hurriedly she turned to face him—this had gone far enough. 'You are a beautiful young woman,' he told her, his voice still speculative. 'You appear to have everything in the right place.' His eyes did a tour of her figure, lingering slightly over her breasts and hips and making her wish she'd worn her suit with its concealing jacket instead of the clinging top and jeans. She felt the colour come up under her skin and knew he had witnessed it.

'Do you think I might be allowed to get on with the work I came here to do?' she said coldly. Lawson Alexander was too astute by far—before she knew it he would have made her lose her temper and she would have revealed everything there was to know. 'I would have thought an apology more in line than this . . . this enquiry into my—love life.'

'Or lack of love life,' he came back quickly. Then, 'How can I apologise for kissing you when you still think I'm a snob?'

So it had stung that she'd called him a snob—she knew she owed him an apology for that. During her restless night she had realised it just wasn't true. 'I no longer think you're a snob,' was the best apology she could come out with.

'Pray tell me,' he said, and she knew he was being sarcastic, 'what revealing light came to you to make you change your mind. It can't be that my kiss did its work for me after all.'

'Don't be funny,' Ivory said daringly—she had forgotten during the last ten minutes that he was her boss. She remembered their respective positions now as she explained in a quiet voice, 'It came to me that a snob wouldn't have made me wear my suit jacket and then walked with me through this plushy hotel—and the one we went to while I was wearing it. And . . . and a snob would never have introduced a secretary to one of his closest friends.' She felt embarrassed when she had finished, but was glad she'd got that off her chest. It was impossible though for her to look at him, and she went on hurriedly to cover her embarrassment, 'Do you think I could get on with some work now?'

Lawson didn't answer her question, but said mysteriously, 'Michael whatever his name is wants his head looking at.'

Ivory took it that their conversation was over and was glad of it as she seated herself before the typewriter. Not waiting for Lawson to say any more, she got on with the work she had left yesterday.

When Lawson went out, briefcase in hand, in time for his ten o'clock meeting, she was beginning to feel more at ease. He really was a most disturbing man, she thought, pausing in her typing. She could hardly credit that she had, in part, discussed Michael with him when, her pride badly bruised, she had found it almost too difficult to tell her own mother. Even then she had been unable to tell her the real reason Michael had thrown her over, and yet if she hadn't put a stop to the questions Lawson had been asking, she had a very definite feeling she would have finished up with him knowing everything.

It didn't take long to finish the work she had to do. She had been to the dining room for her lunch, and was back in her own room when Lawson knocked on her door in the early afternoon. She had been undecided whether to leave his key at the desk for him to pick up after she'd locked his door, but thought he wouldn't be very pleased if he came up expecting her to have it and then had to go down again to collect it.

Feeling suddenly shy, then shrugging it off as being silly she opened the door to him. 'I've left everything on the desk,' she said in greeting. 'I'll just get you the key.' She left him at the door while she went to fetch his key, but just as she picked it up the phone in her room rang, causing her to hesitate.

'Answer your phone,' Lawson instructed her, seeming in no hurry.

'You'd better come in,' she told him, thinking he might have further instructions for her—she could see no other reason why he just didn't take his key and go.

Picking up the phone, she thought it might be one of the hotel staff, though what they could want with her she had no idea. But the voice she heard after saying, 'Hello,' down the instrument was not a voice of anyone in the hotel, but that of Jan Hansen.

'Hello, Jan,' she said, surprise making her voice sound welcoming. From the corner of her eye she saw Lawson stiffen when he heard who her caller was, and she hoped they weren't going to have another row when she came off the phone. For it seemed now that in some way he had an aversion to her being friendly with Jan, and she had already established to her satisfaction that it wasn't caused by snobbery.

'I wanted to speak with you before you left, to wish you a good flight.'

'Why, thank you, Jan! It was thoughtful of you to telephone.'

'My pleasure. I had lunch with Lawson today, he tells me you are leaving this afternoon. You will not forget your promise to dine with me when I come to London?'

Ivory couldn't remember exactly promising that, but saw no reason why she shouldn't dine with him. 'I shall look forward to it,' she told him pleasantly.

'I'm not sure yet of the exact date—May I have your phone number? I expect you prefer me to ring you at home rather than at your office', he added thoughtfully.

She had turned her back on Lawson as her conversation with Jan continued, but as she gave Jan her telephone number she heard an impatient movement behind her, and guessed she had better finish the call while Lawson was still containing himself. With Jan's repeated promise that he would telephone her when he came to London, she replaced the receiver and turned to face her employer.

'That was Jan,' she said needlessly.

Lawson gave her a look that said, 'What else is new?' 'Be ready in an hour,' he said shortly. 'We're leaving this afternoon.'

'So Jan said.'

She wished she hadn't said that, for he gave her a short look, half impatient, half angry, and held out his hand. Uncomprehendingly, she stared from his hand up to his face.

'Key,' he said distinctly. 'Perhaps I might have my key— unless your phone call has so befuddled your brain that you can't remember where you put it.'

It took her a few seconds to find it. She'd had it in her hand when she'd been talking to Jan. She retraced her step back to the phone, discovered it wasn't on the platform that housed the telephone, then dropping her eyes to the bed saw she had placed it there while talking to Jan.

The key in her hand, she took it over to where Lawson was standing. 'I'll be ready,' she said, handing the key over. She wasn't surprised when he didn't answer her—she hadn't expected him to somehow.

The flight to London was uneventful. As soon as they were airborne, Lawson buried himself in some papers from his briefcase and seemed completely oblivious to Ivory's presence. Not that she wanted him to talk to her—she couldn't wait for the flight to end, and with it, the end of her brief though never-to-be-forgotten association with him.

Expecting to part from him at London Airport, she was taken out of this belief by his, 'Come with me,' as she stood wondering which way to go. It wasn't necessary for him to carry her own small case as well as his own luggage, but she was learning better than to argue with him.

When a uniformed chauffeur came smartly up to them and relieved Lawson of the luggage, taking hers also and placing it in the boot of a gleaming Rolls, she found it impossible to refrain from voicing her objection.

'I can find my own way home,' she said shortly.

Lawson's look clearly said, 'Don't be ridiculous', but she was glad he was proving to have better control of his tongue than she was. For had he said it, she felt sure the kick on his shins her feet had been longing to deliver ever since he had come to her room for his key would not have been held back.

For all her tumultuous thoughts, she managed to thank the chauffeur politely as he saw her inside the luxurious interior of the car. And once they were on their way with Lawson once more working on whatever seemed so vitally important that he couldn't waste another minute, she settled back and paused to wonder at the violent emotions he had the power to arouse within her. She could never remember wanting to so much as raise a hand to anybody before she had met him.

Soon the Rolls was driving into surroundings that were familiar to her, and at her involuntary movement, Lawson showed he was not so engrossed in the figures before him as she had thought, for he looked up enquiringly from his paper work.

'I . . . I thought the driver might want directions to where I live,' she explained, stammering because of the suddenness of Lawson's attention.

He leaned forward and slid back the glass partition.

'Miss Dutton will tell you where to turn off, George.'

Ivory gave George directions, and shortly afterwards the Rolls was gliding up to the kerb outside the Victorian house where she and Mandy shared a flat.

The chauffeur was helping her alight from the car before she was able to reach for the door, and while she waited for her case, she found Lawson standing on the pavement beside her. She stood in silence; now she came to think of it, she had enjoyed the work she had done for him. It had been mind-gripping matter—but for the rest of her trip to Amsterdam she had very mixed feelings, and though she thought some parting remark was necessary could not think of a thing she wanted to say to him.

Holding out her hand for her case, she felt superfluous when George placed her case into Lawson's outstretched hand. 'I'll carry it in for you,' he said, brushing aside any protest she would have made.

She saw old Mr Phillips, the ground floor tenant, at his usual place by the window, and swallowed her chagrin as she smiled and waved in greeting. There was nothing she could do but precede Lawson up the stone steps to the front door if she didn't want Mr Phillips, not to mention George, having a ringside seat of an ungainly tug-o'-war.

It came to her to wonder as they tramped up the two flights of stairs, past clean if unimaginative dark brown walls, that Lawson was merely carrying her case in order to see where in the building her flat was. She stepped on the thought—why should it possibly interest him? No, she realised instead, after being such a brute, he was at last finding his gentlemanly instincts too much for him.

Gaining the landing where she lived, Ivory inserted her key into the lock of her door and pushed the door open. The sitting room she had left on Monday looked neat, tidy and dearly familiar. The furniture it housed could in no way be called up-to-date, but it was bright with covers she and Mandy had made for the three-piece suite, and most of the woodwork, wooden chairs included, had recently been given a coat of white paint. And shabby though it might seem to someone with Lawson's undoubtedly expensive taste— her eyes caught on a threadbare patch in the carpet—it was home to her and Mandy, and she was glad to be back.

'Thank you for bringing my case up for me,' she said politely, standing with Lawson just inside her sitting room. She could discern nothing from his look, of what he made of her home—but she was glad to see he wasn't turning his nose up either.

He turned his head to look straight into her violet eyes, gave her a hard look she didn't understand, then said, 'I'm grateful you could come to Holland at such short notice. As Jan said, it was lucky you had a passport.'

If he expected her to rise to that, he was mistaken. 'Wasn't it, though?' she said carefully.

She thought a suggestion of a smile lit his eyes at her refusal to be drawn, but it was gone in an instant as he went on to say, 'Take the day off tomorrow—you've earned it.'

'It's not necessary for me to have the day off—I've barely done anything today,' she argued, and suddenly they were both tight-lipped. She knew he didn't care for the way she threw his offer back at him, but, she thought furiously, there had been no need for his despicable parting remark which followed:

'If you ever go abroad again, just take care whose bedroom you take it into your head to sleep in—your next room mate might not be so self-restrained as I.'

He got the rise she was sure now he had been after all the time. For Ivory couldn't resist slamming the door hard shut after him, and she could have sworn a roar of satisfied laughter echoed back to her as he went down the stairs.

She returned to her duties in the statistical department the next day. Mr Fletcher showed no surprise at seeing her there, and didn't comment either on the length of time she had been away—was it only on Monday she had left? she caught herself wondering; it seemed like a month.

'Did you enjoy yourself?' Mr Fletcher asked.

'I was working for a good part of the time,' she reminded him.

'Of course,' Mr Fletcher said hastily. He was a good manager and took pains not to upset any of the staff he valued, though he was known to come down heavily on anyone who deserved it. 'But Mr Alexander would see to it that you weren't left feeling lost since you were away from home.'

Ivory thought better than to tell Mr Fletcher that Lawson had the welfare of his staff so much at heart he had been forceful in his efforts to see she was not left alone when the day's work was done, so much so that he had threatened to dismiss her if she didn't dine with him.

'I did dine with him once or twice,' she confessed, and looked up to see what Mr Fletcher made of that.

'Good—good,' he said. 'It can be quite lonely when you're in a new environment and don't know anyone.' Then going on to business 'Collect an expenses form from Finance—if you have any trouble filling it in bring it to me and I'll give you a hand.'

Uncertain why she should need his help, Ivory duly collected her expenses form, explaining in case it was needed that she had been to Holland in place of Dizzy Williams. By the time she had finished jiggling about with what she had spent, the money Lawson had given her and the amount of

Dutch money she had remaining, she had spoilt one form and had to go back for another.

'I should have given you a couple to start with,' the young man she had seen before said cheerfully. 'Dizzy always needs about six attempts before she gets her sums right.'

Ivory completed the second form without a single crossing out. Though in the space where she was meant to list her purchases, instead of itemising the briefs, top, bra and blouse she had bought, she wrote down 'Sundries'. Had she been able to make the purchases in English money what she wouldn't have claimed for them at all, but since the Dutch money she was returning was less than the amount Lawson had given her, she had to claim, she realised, in order to get the figures to agree. When she came to return the Dutch money, however, she found the young clerk, though still cheerful, was adamant that he couldn't take the money.

'But Mr Alexander gave it me as a—a sort of float—he said he'd claim for it on his expenses account.'

'News to me that he had one—but I still can't take it. My books just wouldn't balance.'

No amount of arguing would get him to change his mind. It seemed for all his cheery exterior he was dedicated to his forms and nothing was going to be allowed to make his books show a surplus.

Ivory stood at the counter top thinking hard. Lawson Alexander would have his money back if she had to give it back personally. And he'd have the full amount too. Since the money he had given her had obviously come out of his own pocket, she wasn't having him paying for the things she had bought.

'Just a minute,' she called the young man back as he would have waltzed off with her form. And when he came back, form in hand, she took it from him and scored through her 'Sundries' item, then handed the form back.

Having spent a good deal of the morning in dealing with her expenses, Ivory had only a sandwich for lunch and set about translating the cost of the items Lawson Alexander had paid for into English currency. Only when she was satisfied she had worked it out correctly down to the last penny did she place that amount in an envelope together with the remainder of the Dutch currency he had given her. She then paused to think for a few moments. She had no wish to see him, but thought since he might wonder where the money had come from—though the Dutch currency should tell him—she just couldn't leave the envelope for him to find with no explanation. Taking a piece of the firm's headed notepaper she wrote clearly, 'Finance section decline to take your money—so do I', and signed herself, 'Ivory Dutton'. She felt very satisfied with what she'd done as she pushed the note inside the envelope and sealed it.

Hoping he was out having a business lunch or out doing whatever high-powered business executives did in their lunch break—though apart from taking time out to lunch with Jan, from what she could remember Lawson was in the habit of working through his lunch hour—Ivory climbed the stairs to the suite of offices she knew he had on the top floor.

It was the first time she had ever been on that floor, and since all the doors looked the same, she was glad when a young matron, obviously pregnant and carrying a shopping basket, stepped out of a lift some yards away.

'I'm looking for Mr Alexander's office,' Ivory approached the young woman. 'Have you any idea which door I go through?'

'I work for him,' she was told, as the expectant mother moved along the corridor to stop outside one of the natural wood finish doors. Ivory followed her into the room and waited while she placed her shopping basket down on the desk.

'I'm Ivory Dutton from Statistics,' she said, when the young matron turned back to her.

'Oh, you're the secretary who went to Amsterdam. I think Mr Alexander is in—did you want to see him?'

'No, er—no—it isn't necessary for me to take up any of his time,' Ivory stammered, never having thought it would be so easy to get in to see him. Writing him a short and to the point note was vastly different from giving him the money personally. Not that she was afraid of him—she wasn't, she thought with certainty. It was just that he might start arguing, though why he should she couldn't think, because there was nothing to argue over. The money belonged to him and that was that. She delved into her bag for the envelope. 'Could you see he has this?' she asked, and pushed the envelope into the other girl's hand.

'With pleasure.' If she was intrigued with what was inside the envelope, Ivory saw she was too good a secretary to show it.

When the hands of the clock neared five, Ivory gave a sigh of relief. All through the afternoon she had been half expecting a telephone message to say would she present herself on the top floor. She smiled to herself as she made her way home. As if he would bother—he had more important things to do than carpet any of his minions for having the nerve to write a note such as she had written.

Mandy arrived home just after seven and Ivory was glad to see her; she had never met anyone with such a highly developed sense of humour as her petite, dark-haired flatmate.

'Peace, at last—peace!' said Mandy dramatically, dropping her case on the carpet in front of her and closing the door behind her with a thump from her rear. 'Honestly, those kids—you'd think silence has gone out of fashion!'

'Come and take the weight off your feet,' Ivory invited. 'You can take it easy tonight—there's a casserole in the oven. We can eat in a quarter of an hour.'

Ivory returned to the kitchen. She was glad Mandy was back. In the presence of her bright personality she would forget all about Lawson Alexander. She'd known Mandy when they had both lived in Luton, and since Mandy's parents lived next door to her own mother and stepfather, she knew too about her broken engagement and had done her best since they had been sharing to get her to take up some of the invitations out that had come her way.

It was not until they were sitting down to their meal, the fifteen minutes being all Mandy needed to renew her energy after her journey, that she asked Ivory what she had been doing during the week.

'I know you're off men,' she said, not waiting for her answer, 'but honestly, love, you can't go on like this spending night after night cooped up in this flat. I know we go to the cinema from time to time, but you're never going to get over Michael by refusing all the invitations you have to go out. Why, that Alan Brown has asked you out umpteen times to my knowledge . . .'

'Actually, I went to Amsterdam for a few days on Monday,' Ivory interrupted her. She knew Mandy meant well, but she'd heard it all before.

'What—what did you say?' Mandy asked, her mouth dropping open.

'I went to Amsterdam on Monday—came home yesterday,' and as the casserole disappeared, she told Mandy all about it. All, that was, except for the way Lawson Alexander had so brutally kissed her.

'Well!' said Mandy, her quick brain having to work overtime to take in everything Ivory was telling her. And you actually mean to say a Rolls-Royce pulled up outside our door? I wonder what old man Phillips made of that—I take it he was on window-watching duty?' Ivory agreed that he had been. 'Chauffeur-driven, you said,' Mandy recapped. 'What was it like?'

'It was pleasant to drive in,' Ivory stated, not liking to tell Mandy she had been so engrossed in the thoughts of violence Lawson bred in her that she had barely noticed the ride.

'And this Lawson Alexander—he actually came up here to our flat?' Mandy looked around the sitting room-cum-dining room, her eyes obviously doing the same survey Ivory had felt compelled to do when she had invited Lawson in.

'It's home to us,' she inserted quietly.

They fell silent as Mandy nodded in agreement. But after only seconds she was bubbling over with questions. 'Imagine waking up and finding a strange man in the other bed! I bet you nearly died of fright—what's he like to look at—stringy, hairless and sixty?'

'Er—he's—er—quite good-looking in a way,' Ivory got out with difficulty as she watched Mandy's eyes growing larger.

'How old would you say he is?' Mandy asked, her eyes watchful at the faint pink that had come up under her friends complexion.

'Thirty-fiveish,' Ivory returned, having no idea why she was blushing other than that telling her story to Mandy had made it come to life, and she was again experiencing those disturbing feelings Lawson Alexander aroused in her. She saw a shrewd look come into Mandy's clever eyes. 'Don't get any ideas, Mandy,' she implored. 'I went to meet him strictly on business. If you're thinking something romantic happened, forget it—it didn't.' Well, you could hardly call his kiss romantic, it had been more in the nature of a punishment for her having dared to call him a snob. 'In actual fact I found Mr Alexander the most abominable man I've met in a long while.' She didn't know why she laid so much stress on her words—she believed them; it wasn't herself she had to convince, but Mandy.

She could see Mandy was no way to being convinced, so she went on to tell her about Jan Hansen. By the time they went to their beds, she was fairly certain Mandy had forgotten all about Lawson Alexander. Though she paused herself before climbing into bed to wonder if he had yet opened her envelope.

Ivory quickly settled back into the routine of her life before she had been sent to Amsterdam. Three weeks flew by with her barely being aware of it as Amsterdam and the anger she had felt with the man who had returned with her faded. But gradually as those weeks went by, she began to realise that something was different.

At first, she couldn't peg what exactly it was, it was so nebulous. What was it, she wondered, this feeling of light-heartedness, this feeling of being free—uncaring? Nothing special had happened apart from the Amsterdam trip— and anything that had happened then she would sooner draw a veil over. Mandy was out that evening with Adrian, who had lasted longer than most with her friend, so with the flat to herself, Ivory sat down trying to think what had brought about this change in her. Why, she had almost said yes to Alan Brown's invitation to go with him to a party— and she would never have even considered that at one time.

Not since Michael . . . She stopped in mid-thought. That was it. *That was it.* Michael. She'd stopped thinking about Michael.

She tried to think of the last time she'd thought about him, and realised he hadn't popped into her mind since that day she had come home with Lawson Alexander. It delighted her that she was free of her ex-fiancé when at one time she had thought she would be fretting over him for evermore. But she couldn't help but wonder if Lawson Alexander's abrasive attitude hadn't in some way helped work towards a cure. Oh, she didn't like him—she knew that with definite conviction. But his casually voiced jibe of, 'Would I be right in thinking there haven't been any boy-friends for the last six months?' must have jolted her without her being aware of it—and his kiss, loathesome though it was, had been therapeutic by virtue of being the first lips to touch hers since Michael's. It was as though that contact had severed the link that bound her to Michael, she realised now. Oh, she'd cried that night, and Lawson had suggested his kiss had triggered something off—only now was she able to admit he had been right.

The ringing of the telephone cut off any more thoughts she might have on the subject. But the lighthearted feeling persisted as she went to answer it, wondering who it was as she went. It wouldn't be her mother, because she had telephoned her yesterday and she knew she was going with her stepfather to stay with friends in Bristol for a week or so.

Thinking the call must be for Mandy, she was surprised and delighted to hear Jan Hansen's voice saying, 'Hello, is that you Ivory?'

'Why Jan—How lovely to hear from you.'

She remembered he said he would telephone her when he came to London, but as the weeks had gone by, she had thought he would have changed his mind. They spoke for some minutes before he got down to the purpose of his call.

'Would you be free to dine with me tomorrow evening? I know it is short notice, but I am only in London for a few days.'

'I'd be pleased to, Jan,' Ivory said in agreement, and didn't stop to wonder how easy it was to make a date to go out with someone other than Michael.

When Mandy came in, Ivory was in her bedroom going through her wardrobe. 'What gives?' Mandy asked inelegantly, coming into the room and surveying the three dresses Ivory thought might be suitable now hanging on the outside of her wardrobe door.

'I'm going out tomorrow,' she told her, smiling at Mandy's squeal of pleasure. 'Jan—the Dutchman I told you about—phoned, and I was just wondering what to wear.' They both stood back to study the trio of dresses—the pink one she had bought in Amsterdam Ivory thought was far and away the nicest.

'The pink one,' said Mandy unhesitatingly.

'I don't know,' Ivory hedged. Without knowing why she was somehow loath to wear that particular dress. 'I could buy something new in my lunch hour tomorrow—I told you I got a bonus on my last salary cheque, didn't I?' The extra amount in her cheque had puzzled her for a moment until she recalled what Lawson had said about a bonus, and realised he must have given instructions for the payment to be made.

'The pink one,' Mandy repeated.

CHAPTER FIVE

STILL uncertain about the pink dress, Ivory intended searching the shops in her lunch hour on the chance of finding something else suitable to wear. But her lunch hour was cut short by an error in calculation someone in the department had made which consequently threw everything out of gear. As it was Friday and Mr Fletcher wanted everything cleared up ready for a fresh start on Monday, and although she was primarily on the secretarial staff, Ivory along with everyone else was roped in to help. Since Mr Fletcher was always very good about allowing time off if one had something special on, she put her disappointment behind her and took only sufficient of her lunch hour to enable her to eat a sandwich before going back to work again.

Jan called for her promptly at eight, his eyes lighting up when she opened the door to him. His face showed no recollection of having seen her dress before. But she could do better than top it with the jacket of her grey suit this time, and after introducing him to Mandy who was going out later, she went to collect a fine lacy stole from her bedroom.

'I have booked a table at the Fenwick,' Jan told her when they were on their way. 'I thought we might dine at nine if that is suitable to you?'

Ivory warmed to his charming manner, and agreed that that would suit her very well. She was glad now she was wearing pink, the other two dresses weren't really suitable for the illustrious Fenwick, and she confessed to herself at last that the only thing she had against the dress was the suspicion that Lawson Alexander had no intention of claiming for it on his expense account—if indeed his expense account existed.

The evening progressed without strain on either side with an easy flow of conversation running between them. Ivory discovered she was enjoying her evening with Jan much more than she had anticipated she would, and when their meal was finished and he suggested they go into the lounge bar for an after-dinner drink, she was in complete agreement with his suggestion.

However as they went through into the other room her enjoyment of the evening took a sudden and rapid downward trend. For the first person she saw seated across the room was Lawson Alexander. There were quite a few other people in the lounge, so why he should stand out above all others she didn't know. He had seen her too, although his expression did not alter as he recognised her. She saw his eyes slide past her and on to her companion, but she looked away before she saw what, if anything, he made of the fact she was with Jan.

She felt Jan's hand tighten on her arm as she stopped in her tracks. 'Is anything the matter?' he asked, seeming to sense that something had affected her.

'No . . . No,' she replied quickly, turning her head to one side to smile at him.

Then Jan too had spotted Lawson, and the smile he was giving her widened as he exclaimed, 'Well, of all the luck!' and leading her by the arm, made straight for Lawson and his companion.

Lawson was on his feet when they reached him, acknowledging her with a formal, 'Good evening, Ivory,' before turning with his hand outstretched to Jan.

'I've been trying to get you on the phone since yesterday,' Jan was saying, while Ivory glanced to see Lawson's companion was a dark-haired creature equal in good looks and sophistication to the red-haired Sheba Nightingale Lawson had introduced her to in Amsterdam.

'I've been out of the country for a week or so,' she tuned in to what Lawson was telling Jan. 'Arrived back today.' Then Lawson was turning to his companion. 'Louise, allow me to introduce Ivory Dutton and Jan Hansen—Louise Greening.'

The introductions made, Ivory heard Lawson asking Jan if they would care to join them, and wanting desperately for Jan to say no, she could do nothing but return an agreeable smile when Jan looked in her direction.

Lawson indicated that she should take the seat he had just vacated on the settee beside Louise, and seemed unaware that Jan was hovering to take the chair nearest to her while Jan was forced to take the chair furthest away, and was sitting near to Louise. Then Lawson was summoning a waiter and asking Ivory what she would like to drink.

'A Martini, please,' she said, saying the first alcoholic drink that came into her head. She couldn't remember having one before and hoped she would like it. It was happening again—just sitting down at the same table as Lawson Alexander and that disturbing feeling he aroused in her was making itself felt, so that she wasn't thinking clearly enough to ask for the drink she would probably have liked better—a medium dry sherry.

'I take it you arrived yesterday, Jan?' Lawson was asking. 'Here for a few days?'

'I have concluded the business I came here to do today,' Jan told him, 'but alas, I have to be back in Holland on Monday morning.'

Their drinks arrived and conversation became general,

during which Ivory heard Louise telling Jan she and Lawson had been to the theatre, and while she was outlining to him some of the plot of the play, Lawson turned his head in Ivory's direction.

'Your drink isn't going down very fast—is it to your liking?'

Trust him to remember she'd ordered a medium dry sherry on the two occasions she had dined with him! 'Perfect, thank you,' she told him, trying to sound cool, but feeling anything but, since he seemed to be giving her his undivided attention. Then as he continued to look at her as if waiting for her to add more, she found herself confessing honestly because there didn't seem any point in pretending otherwise, 'I don't drink an awful lot.'

'Would you prefer something else?'

She felt herself go hot—any minute now she'd have everyone's attention on her. 'No, thank you, Mr Alexander —I'm quite enjoying this.'

A glimmer of a smile lit his eyes at her prim assurances, but he let the matter drop. 'Do you think since this is a social occasion, you could drop the Mr Alexander?'

Ivory wrenched her eyes from his dark look to see Louise still holding forth to Jan on the play she had seen.

'Certainly,' Ivory replied, but could not bring herself to add, 'Lawson', and since the other two were not tuned into their conversation, she felt she had a very real opportunity of clearing up something that had been bothering her.

'Did you claim for this dress on your expense account?' she asked baldly, feeling the colour rush to her face when Lawson's eyes scanned not only her earnest face, but the dress that covered her body as well.

'What makes you think I wouldn't?' he asked smoothly, seeming not to notice her blush.

'The . . . the young man in Finance seemed unaware that

you had an expense account,' she stammered, knowing that
if she'd hoped to disconcert him by her direct question, she
was far from succeeding.

'And that bothers you?'

'Of course it bothers me,' Ivory snapped, just managing in
time to keep her voice down if she didn't want Jan and
Louise to know what they were talking about.

'And what will you do if I say I haven't claimed for it?'
he asked, his face taking on a tight line. 'Put the money in an
envelope and leave it with one of my secretaries?'

They faced each other like two warring invaders, only
their eyes showing there was anything amiss as Ivory strove
to keep her face from showing any of her feelings as
Lawson's words reached her. From his expression she could
glean nothing, but there was a fire in his eyes that told her
she had annoyed him by the way she had returned his
money—her note wasn't mentioned. And then the fire she
thought she had seen had gone, and he was saying smoothly:

'Relax, Miss Dutton—I can assure you we have our own
finance section in senior management.'

He still hadn't answered her question fully, and she
supposed she would have to be content with what he had
told her, for she wasn't likely to go to his office to seek him
out and try to pin him down to giving her a more definite
answer—come to that, she'd like to see anyone try to pin
him down if he felt like being obscure.

'Another drink, Ivory?' Jan's voice broke into her
thoughts and she looked across at him to smile her refusal.
'In that case I think we will be on our way. Nice to have
met you, Louise.'

Some of her earlier pleasure at being in Jan's company
returned on the drive home, and as he escorted her up to
her door she found herself thinking what a nice person he

was. At the door of her flat she turned to thank him for the evening and found he had both hands on her shoulders imprisoning her. When he began to lower his head towards her, his intention to kiss her goodnight obvious, Ivory turned her head to one side.

'No,' she whispered softly.

Instantly Jan pulled his head up. 'Too soon?' he asked.

She knew he meant too soon in their friendship. 'Too—soon,' she echoed.

She endorsed her opinion of what a nice person he was, for he took her refusal to allow him to kiss her without argument, and promptly asked her if he could see her again the following evening.

When Monday morning arrived she had been out with Jan three nights in succession, and as she took the cover off her typewriter holding back a yawn, she decided it was just as well Jan was flying back to Holland this morning, for she doubted she would have lasted the pace of another evening out without an early night in between.

By the time three o'clock arrived that afternoon, she found that for one of the few times in her working career she was watching the clock. Only another two hours and she could go home and put her feet up. She had the dickens of a headache and decided if it wasn't any better after her evening meal, she would take some aspirin—something she very rarely did. Having to concentrate extra hard on her work, she was unaware that Timmy, the office boy, had been speaking to her until she looked away from her work.

'I'm sorry, Timmy—what did you say?'

'Mr Fletcher wants to see you pronto,' said Timmy, who one of the girls had said would have to be taken down a peg or two before he was much older.

Ivory left her desk hoping Mr Fletcher wasn't going to ask

her to work late that night. But when he explained what he wanted to see her about, she would far rather it had been to ask her to stay on after five.

'Ah—Ivory,' he said when she had closed the door to his office. 'Would you go along to Mr Alexander's office?'

'Mr Alexander's office?' Ivory repeated. If there was some errand to be completed, surely Timmy should be the one to go.

'That's right. He wants to see you straight away.'

'Wants to see *me*?' She knew she shouldn't be arguing the point, but felt she would rather go anywhere than to the top floor.

Mr Fletcher looked at her as though understanding her bewilderment; it wasn't often any of his staff were summoned to the executive suite. 'Straight away if you would, Ivory. It wouldn't do to keep Mr Alexander waiting.'

Wishing she was more in command than she felt, she had no alternative other than to do as Mr Fletcher requested. Though what Lawson Alexander wanted to see her about she couldn't think. Her head was still throbbing painfully, so instead of taking the stairs as she had the last time she had gone in search of his office, she used the lift. He couldn't be calling her up to let rip into her about the note she sent him, she reasoned—he'd had his chance to do that on Friday. With his expertise he could have done that quite well without either Jan or Louise being aware what was happening. Her headache was clouding her thought, she realised, as she stepped out of the lift. Even Lawson Alexander wouldn't take one of his staff to task in public. That must be the reason he wanted to see her, she decided. If he had been abroad again then this must be his first opportunity to censure her about it—even though somehow he had found time to see that the wages section knew she was to be paid a bonus.

She gave up thinking of other reasons why she had been sent for as she tapped on the door she remembered going through before. It was useless speculating—she'd know soon enough what she'd done to displease him; she didn't flatter herself he had sent for her for any other reason than to remonstrate with her over something.

The young woman she had seen before was busy at her typewriter when she went in. 'Oh, hello,' she said in a friendly way. 'Would you go through that door.' She pointed to a door behind her. 'Mrs Stavely's expecting you.'

More mystified than ever, Ivory gave her a suggestion of a smile and went behind her through the door she had indicated into another larger, though equally well appointed office, where a grey-haired woman was reading through some typed sheets in front of her.

'Miss Dutton?' she enquired, peering over the top of half-moon spectacles.

'Yes,' Ivory admitted, wondering if Mrs Stavely would then direct her through the door she could see to the right of her. She wondered if there would be another woman in that room and yet another door—this could go on for what was left of the afternoon, she thought, feeling not unlike Alice. Her head was aching unbearably and she'd be glad when this was all over and she was back at the flat.

'Would you take a seat for a few moments—Mr Alexander will see you at four. I'm Mrs Stavely, Mr Alexander's senior secretary, by the way.'

Ivory thought it was very friendly of Mrs Stavely to tell her so, and seated herself in the chair as the senior secretary had suggested while Mrs Stavely returned to whatever she was reading. A surreptitious glance at her watch told her she had five minutes to go before Lawson Alexander would see her—so much for Mr Fletcher saying he wanted to see her straight away! She'd given up wondering what he wanted to see her about and tried to sit composed on her chair so as not to disturb his secretary.

Ivory looked at her with growing admiration when at thirty seconds to the appointed time, without so much as looking at her watch, Mrs Stavely pressed a button on the intercom in front of her, and in reply to the, 'Yes,' that was Lawson, even the distortion of the equipment couldn't hide those crisp tones, Mrs Stavely told him, 'Miss Dutton is here.'

'Would you ask Miss Dutton to come in.'

Ivory left her seat as Mrs Stavely looked across at her. There was only one other door—it had to be that one.

Lawson's office was bigger than the other two, and apart from the obvious desk and leather-upholstered chair looked less like an office than any other room she had seen in the building. There were three or four leather-cushioned easy chairs and two or three occasional tables dotted about. A couple of pictures adorned the pale green walls and her feet sank into pale green deep-pile carpet as she entered the room. She guessed business here was shrewd and sharp and that visitors were cushioned by the environment into feeling at ease before any bargaining began.

Lawson Alexander looked just as she'd pictured he would behind his wood-panelled desk. He was wearing a dark grey suit with a crisp striped shirt, his eyes sharp and alert as he told her to come and take the chair nearest to him. It was the only straight-backed chair in the room other than his own, and Ivory guessed this was where Mrs Stavely sat to take his dictation.

Having obeyed his request to be seated, she could have wished the chair was away from the window, as he observed with his terse opening remark:

'You look tired.'

'I have a headache.' Not a very promising start—but then if he was going to be aggressive, she wasn't about to take it lying down.

'Too many late nights?'

It was none of his business. 'Probably.' He knew it all—why argue with him?

Her short answer didn't please him; the cool look on his face told her that. 'Perhaps it is just as well Jan has returned home,' he said shortly.

'Why?' she bit back at him before she could stop herself. 'And who says it was Jan who caused me to have late nights?'

'Unless you've suddenly changed drastically, I'm sure it must be Jan. In Holland you gave me a distinct impression you were off men for good—I can't see a girl of your type running two men at once.'

Girl of her type? Just because she spent three days or so with him in Amsterdam—on business, she hastily tacked on—he thought he knew all there was to know about her. Even while her own aggression was stirring itself, she secretly admitted he was right, of course—it wasn't in her to date more than one man at a time. But it irritated her that he should know it.

'What I do with my private life is no concern of anyone's but mine,' she said flatly. And if he couldn't read into that, that she was quietly telling him to mind his own business, then she'd tell him outright if he argued the point. She knew she had got through to him by the way a muscle jerked in his jaw as her words hit his ears, but she was quite unrepentant as they stared at each other in what she thought was mutual dislike.

'It becomes the concern of the Alexander Corporation when it affects you so that you can't do your work properly,' he told her coldly.

'Not do my work properly?' she gasped. Good grief, today was the first day she hadn't felt up to scratch. She was sure it hadn't shown in her work ... Could she be sure of that, though? she paused to wonder. Her head was pounding too badly for her to recall any of the work she had done that day—it had been rather humdrum stuff, she managed to recall, which had enabled her to do the work semi-automatically. But surely if her work had been at fault Mr Fletcher would have mentioned it—she couldn't believe he would send her to Lawson Alexander to be disciplined.

'Is that why I'm here?' she asked abruptly. 'To be chastised about my work?'

Lawson gave her a long level look before replying, during which time Ivory wished if that was the reason he would get on with it, so that she could crawl out of his office and go and lick her wounded self-respect in private.

'I have every confidence in Mr Fletcher's ability to run his department,' he said at length. So that wasn't why she was here. 'As a matter of fact,' he went on, 'I've heard nothing but glowing reports of you from him.'

'Oh.' She wondered if he had progress reports on every secretary in the building, and couldn't believe a man in his position would want to be bothered with such mundane matters.

'I've decided, after seeing the splendid job you made of the work I gave you in Amsterdam, that you would suit perfectly,' he said to her mystification. 'But naturally it was only courtesy to have a word with Mr Fletcher before I told you.'

She was glad he thought well of her work, of course, and could do nothing to stem the feeling of pride that flowed through her that he should tell her so. But she felt herself completely in the dark as to the rest of what he was telling her.

'I'm sorry to be obtuse, but I seem to be missing the point,' she said, wrinkling her brow, prepared to blame her headache for the fact her normally quick-to-catch-on brain was letting her down badly. 'You had a word with Mr Fletcher before you told me—what?'

'Didn't I say?' Lawson asked urbanely, when she was sure he knew very well she had no idea what he was talking about. 'I want you to be my junior secretary.'

'What?' She hadn't meant to blurt the word out like that—but the shock of what he had just said was rocking her sideways.

'I said I want you to be my junior secretary,' he repeated clearly, for all, she thought, he must know she had heard him perfectly well the first time. 'What's the matter— doesn't the idea appeal to you?' He took a few moments to study her bewildered expression, then told her smoothly, 'If it would make you feel any better you would be working mainly under Mrs Stavely.'

'I . . . I . . .' His words gave her a fair indication that he knew how she felt about him.

'You needn't give me your answer straight away—take tonight and think it over. You can let Mrs Stavely know your decision in the morning. Jenny will be leaving in a few weeks to await the arrival of her baby, so I would like some- one to start straight away to keep things running smoothly.' He paused briefly to let that sink in, then added, 'The work is more challenging than the work you're doing now, so naturally there would be a substantial increase in salary.'

Ivory tried to think clearly, but it was no good. She'd come up here expecting to hear anything other than what Lawson had just told her. She knew, or thought she knew, she didn't want to work for him, even if it was 'mainly under Mrs Stavely'. While at the same time she had to admit the idea of a challenging job appealed to her. She just couldn't get very excited about working in Statistics, yet Mr Fletcher was such a wonderful man to work for, how could she possibly consider coming to work for a man she suspected would be a tyrant if her work didn't meet with his approval?

Conscious that her interview with Lawson was over, she made to rise to her feet, and found Lawson standing very close to her so that she had to tilt her head back to look into his face.

'Your headache's a stormer, isn't it?' he said in a surprisingly sympathetic tone, noticing the look of pain in the eyes that looked at him and away. 'Have you taken anything for it?'

'I was going to when I got home.'

He didn't say what he thought of females who were unable to take immediate preventative action, but his eyes, still watchful, told her what he thought.

'I have to go out myself shortly—collect your coat, I'll take you home.'

His words were even more of a surprise to her than his sympathy. 'But,' she protested, when the idea of lying flat out on her bed sounded like Shangri-la to her, 'Mr Fletcher . . .'

'Go and get your coat,' he repeated as if she hadn't spoken. 'I'll be outside in my car in five minutes.'

Naturally she had to go to Mr Fletcher's office to tell him she was going home, but once there, she found Mrs Stavely had already rung down and acquainted him with the news that Ivory was unwell and was going home.

'I hope you'll feel better tomorrow, my dear,' he said, echoing Lawson's sympathy. 'I expect all the excitement has been too much for you—a great feather in the cap of Statistics to have one of our secretaries promoted to Mr

Alexander's secretary.' His face was fairly beaming, and Ivory didn't have the heart to tell him she hadn't yet made up her mind. It didn't seem to bother him at all that he would be one secretary short.

It wasn't the Rolls waiting outside as she had half expected. Lawson was standing beside a speedy-looking Aston Martin. Ivory felt his eyes on her as he helped her into the passenger seat, and wanted to shrug his hand away. She only had a headache, for goodness' sake!

She was being a real crosspatch, she realised as Lawson eased in the clutch and pulled away from the kerb. Whatever his faults, and she admitted he had plenty only she was feeling too lethargic to list them, he had an inate courtesy that came through time and time again.

This was proved yet again when he unerringly pulled up outside the house where she lived, even though he'd only been there once before, and insisted on seeing her to her door. And once there he went with her into her sitting room, asking quietly, 'Where do you keep your aspirin?'

Ivory was too surprised to question his enquiry, and without conscious thought found herself saying, 'In the bathroom cabinet.'

He stood beside her while she swallowed two of the tablets, then returned the bottle to the bathroom before coming to stand over her. 'I should go and lie down and let the tablets get to work on you,' he said, seeming larger than ever as he loomed over her.

'I think I will,' she told him, her head too painful for her to realise that was about the first time she had agreed with him about anything.

He was at the door about to go when she found herself asking a question it seemed quite important for her to know the answer to—for she couldn't think why he wanted her to be his secretary when he had so many others he could choose from.

'Why me?' she asked out of the blue, and was glad he caught on straight away and she didn't need to explain her question, for all it was some time before he answered, as he just stood and looked back at her. Then a ghost of a smile crossed his features.

'Who else could read my writing?' he asked in return, then he was gone.

When Mandy came home a few hours later, Ivory had been able to drop off to sleep and had awakened to find that the giants playing the 1812 Overture full belt in her head were now playing pianissimo.

'Sorry I haven't done anything towards getting a meal, Mandy—I left work early with a bad head and went to sleep,' she explained.

'That's all right,' Mandy said cheerfully. 'How's the head now?' and at Ivory's assurances that it was fine, gave her a hard look as though to discern she was telling the truth and noticed the troubled frown on her brow.

'Your head might be better, but something's bothering you,' she said with candour. 'What if I nip round to the chipper—it will save cooking. Then if you want an impartial ear you can tell me what's worrying you.'

Over fish and chips Ivory told Mandy about Lawson Alexander's unexpected offer for her to be his junior secretary. But she had her doubts about Mandy's impartiality when she answered, 'But that's great—I can't think why you're hesitating.'

'I'm not even sure I like the man,' Ivory began. And when Mandy looked at her as if waiting for more, she wriggled uncomfortably and muttered as though it was being dragged out of her, 'I find him ... disturbing somehow.'

'Disturbing?'

It was no good, she could never explain to Mandy the feeling that churned up inside her every time she was in his company. 'He's so—I don't know . . .' she tried. 'Well, he can be impossibly rude for one thing. He seems to want to know what makes me tick—and what he doesn't know he guesses at.'

'And comes up with the right answer?'

'Invariably.'

'Well, since he's told you you'd be working under this Mrs Stavely, I shouldn't think you'll have much to do with him. And besides the rise in salary, from what you've said of your Mr Fletcher's reaction to the offer, the whole statistical department is going to have egg on its face if you don't accept.'

Ivory went to bed early that night and felt the benefit of it when she awakened with a clear, pain-free head. With mixed feelings she made her way to the office wondering as she went how she could possibly turn the job down. She wondered too if she could ask Mr Fletcher if he would have her back if the job on the top floor didn't work out. But she knew inwardly that once she had accepted the job, her pride would make her work at it to make it a success—there would be no turning back.

'Good morning, Ivory, feeling better?' Mr Fletcher was one of the first in and came up to her desk as she uncovered her typewriter. 'Won't be doing that down here for very much longer, eh?' he added jovially, still in the same happy frame of mind he had been in yesterday. He turned to talk to one of the other girls just as she would have said, 'Mr Fletcher,' and called him back.

Her work that morning seemed to be more unexciting than usual. The word 'Challenging' seemed to be printed before her on every fresh sheet of paper she rolled into her typewriter, and at half past eleven she knew Lawson Alexander had won. She would go and be his junior secretary, but she wasn't going to sit down under any of his sharp-tongued, acid comments. If he wanted a 'yes-girl', he had picked on the wrong one!

Leaving her desk, she went and told Mr Fletcher where she was going, and before she could change her mind was in the lift on her way up to the executive suite to tell Mrs Stavely of her decision.

'Mrs Stavely has been expecting you,' the girl Lawson had called Jenny told her when she went through the door to the office that would be hers in a short while. 'Would you like to go through?'

Mrs Stavely looked up as she entered the room. 'Good morning, Miss Dutton—have you come to tell me your decision?' she asked without preamble.

'Yes, I've thought it over—and yes, I'd like the job.' It was out—what happened now was in the lap of the gods.

'Good, I'm so glad,' said Mrs Stavely, giving her a warm smile. Then getting down to basics, 'Jenny wants to go at the end of the month, so if you could be prepared to come on Monday, I'll fix it with Mr Fletcher,' she said, taking Ivory's gasp of surprise to mean she couldn't leave Mr Fletcher so soon. She then went on to talk about salary and as Ivory's eyes widened, she said, 'Don't worry, my dear, you'll earn every penny of it.' Then as if that sounded too ominous, she went on, 'Don't get me wrong. Very often we're pushed to our full capacity—Mr Alexander is a demon for work, but provided you do your work well, you'll find him a wonderful man to work for.'

Ivory doubted this, but thought better than to say so; it was obvious Mrs Stavely thought the world of him. 'I'm to come straight up here on Monday, then, am I?' she clarified.

'Yes, that's right. Jenny will show you the ropes.' Mrs Stavely rose from her chair. 'We'll go and have a word with her, shall we?'

Jenny Cuthbert welcomed her successor with a friend-liness that made Ivory wish she weren't leaving. It would have been pleasant working with her, she thought, while at the same time realising that if it wasn't for the impending arrival of Cuthbert junior, the need to take her out of Statistics wouldn't have arisen.

After a quiet weekend which involved doing the usual household chores, going to the cinema with Mandy, and taking herself off for a long walk, Ivory dressed with care on Monday morning. She had half decided to wear her grey suit—it was her best and comparatively new—but it had associations with that trip to Holland, so instead she donned a navy skirt and top and was moderately pleased that she looked smart and businesslike to start in her new job as junior secretary to Lawson Alexander. She only hoped her brain was up to everything Jenny had to teach her.

But when she reached the room she was to share with Jenny for the next few weeks, she found no Jenny, and un-sure what she did until she arrived, was pleased when Mrs Stavely came in from her own office. Though her spirits all but deserted her at what Mrs Stavely had to tell her.

'I'm afraid we shall have to battle along as best we can,' Mrs Stavely greeted her. 'Jenny had a hospital appointment last Friday, and they've suggested she rest as much as possible until the baby comes—Mr Alexander is insistent that she does so.'

CHAPTER SIX

'You mean Jenny won't be here to show me my job?'

'With Mr Alexander insisting that Jenny obeys her doctor's instructions, I'm afraid not. Not to worry,' Mrs Stavely added, showing her it was her unflappability that had helped to secure her the job as senior secretary. 'We'll manage somehow.'

Throughout that day Ivory tried to bother Mrs Stavely as little as possible. Fortunately Lawson was abroad on business again, and although she suspected Mrs Stavely still had a fair amount to do in his absence she was able to spend more time with her than she would have been able to otherwise.

Ivory found the work she was doing a complete contrast from the work in Statistics. It was so much more interesting, for one thing. A new world was opening up before her now she was more in touch with what went on behind the scenes of big business. She found it so absorbing that by the end of the week she wondered how she had managed to stay with Mr Fletcher for so long. And as that thought came, she couldn't help but feel nervous in case her work wasn't up to Jenny's standard. Lawson, she knew, would have no compunction in sending her back to Statistics if her work didn't suit him, and the thought of returning to her old department after her glimpse of the work that went on at this level was something she didn't think she could face.

The uncertainty she was feeling, knowing she couldn't have achieved as much this week as Jenny who had been doing the work for five years, must have been showing, she realised, as Mrs Stavely came in and paused to give her an enquiring look.

'I was just wondering if I've been of any use this week,' Ivory said in a rush, betraying her nervousness.

'Of course you have!' Mrs Stavely exclaimed. 'Mr Alexander told me you turned out perfect work—he was right.' Ivory felt a glow of pleasure that Lawson thought that about her work, but hated the feeling of not having pulled her weight. 'Don't worry about it,' Mrs Stavely added. 'Another couple of weeks and you'll be going flat out—everything will fall into place and you'll wonder what you were worried about.'

Ivory went home in a happy frame of mind, thinking perhaps Mrs Stavely might be right—after all, she already knew far more about the job today than she had on Monday.

Mandy had been away on another relief teaching post, and had came in later that night wanting to know how her first week had gone down. 'And what's your overpowering ogre like to work for?' she asked, when Ivory had given her a rough outline in the difference between her work in Statistics from her work in the executive suite. 'I'll bet he's not half as bad as you anticipated.'

'I wouldn't know—he's been abroad. I shall know on Monday, though. Mrs Stavely says he always likes to get back to England for the weekend—probably likes to get back to his harem.' As soon as the words left her lips Ivory realised they were a little unfair; from her own personal knowledge she knew of only two females Lawson associated with.

'Harem?' Mandy queried, her face showing avid interest. 'Do tell—what have you found out?'

'Er—nothing,' Ivory was forced to confess. 'But there's

always been plenty of talk that he plays as hard as he works.'

'Sour grapes, I expect,' said Mandy, looking disappointed.
Then since there was nothing more exciting coming her way
about Lawson Alexander, 'Oh well,' she said, getting up out
of her chair, 'I suppose I'd better go and make myself
beautiful—Adrian will be here before I'm ready if I don't
look sharp.'

The phone rang some time after Mandy had left with her
date Adrian, and with pleased surprise Ivory heard Jan's
voice on the line.

'You're in London again?' she asked, while thinking he
hadn't said anything to her about coming over again so soon
the last time she had seen him.

'No, unfortunately not,' his voice sounded regretful. 'I
am telephoning from Holland—but if I were free from
business commitments it is in London I should like to be at
this moment.'

'Oh.' They had got on very well when he had been over
here, but she wasn't sure what to make of his remark, if
anything. It came to her then that he wouldn't be ringing up
all the way from Holland just for a chat—and at the same
time she realised why he might be ringing. 'Have you been
trying to get in touch with Lawson?' Lawson's first name
came out easily, making her aware that she always thought of
him by his first name even if she couldn't openly address him
so.

'Now why should I want to do that?' There was a teasing
note in Jan's voice that had her smiling even though she
knew he couldn't see her.

'I—Lawson's been in Denmark all this week—I . . . just
wondered.'

It appeared Jan had rung up just for a chat after all, and
as the minutes ticked by and he seemed in no hurry to
finish his call, she had to force herself to remember that in

his financial bracket the cost of the call would mean nothing to him.

By the time his call came to a close, she had told him about being promoted to Lawson's junior secretary and had received Jan's sincere congratulations.

'Since you will no doubt be able to see Lawson much more easily than I will, perhaps you would pass on a message for me?' Jan asked her. '—I would ring him myself tomorrow, but will be in the middle of a weekend conference.' It wasn't all play for these millionaires, Ivory thought. She knew of at least two who worked very hard indeed. 'Would you mind telling him I have been able to find the book he was after?'

'Book?' Ivory repeated, not sure the word had come across the wires accurately.

'Book,' Jan affirmed. 'Lawson has quite a collection of rare books—he particularly wanted the one I have been able to locate.'

When Jan finally rang off, Ivory discovered they had been talking for twenty minutes. She made a note and put it in her purse to remind her to tell Lawson about the book. She loved books herself and would love to see his collection. She turned her thoughts away, knowing she would never get to see it, and thought instead of the pleasure in Jan's voice when he was talking to her. He had said he would be coming over again shortly—said he would telephone her again . . .

Lawson was already in his office when she arrived on Monday. She knew he was in even before Mrs Stavely told her. It was ridiculous, she knew, but she seemed to sense in the very air she breathed that everything had changed up a gear—the whole atmosphere seemed to take on a new urgency.

While the door between her office and Mrs Stavely's office stayed open because of the constant trips she had to

make into the other secretary's room, Lawson's door stayed
firmly shut. Though once when she was in the other office,
she heard his voice come clearly over the intercom, 'Would
you come through, Mrs Stavely, please?'

Knowing there was a door leading from his room into the
corridor outside, she suspected that would be the door he
would use if he went out to lunch, but couldn't help hoping
he might come to see Mrs Stavely while she was there so she
could tell him about the book. She didn't know how much
importance he placed on the information she had for him,
but when after a hectic morning she went out to her own
lunch and came back to see his door was still closed to, she
knew she had to let him have his message without further
delay—that or else sit like a cat on hot bricks all afternoon
waiting on the offchance that he would appear.

Glancing at the intercom, she was about to flick the
switch that would connect her to his office when her throat
suddenly went dry. This was ridiculous, she told herself—
but ridiculous or not, she had to swallow before her hands
once more reached for the switch.

'Did you want Mr Lawson for something, Ivory?' Mrs
Stavely had come into the room, her eagle eye noting
Ivory's hovering fingers.

'I have a message for Mr Alexander from a friend of his,'
Ivory explained. 'I thought I'd tell him over the intercom.'

'If it's personal I should pop in and see him, dear,' Mrs
Stavely said kindly.

'W-won't he mind—I mean, he might be in the middle
of something?'

If Mrs Stavely thought a personal visit couldn't be any
less of an interruption than a dismembered voice breaking
into his train of thought over the intercom, she refrained
from saying so.

'I've found Mr Alexander is capable of concentrating on several things at once,' she said. And reluctantly Ivory pulled her hand away from the machine.

'I should go now—he has some people coming to see him at three,' Mrs Stavely advised.

Ivory smiled wanly in her direction, then walked through into Mrs Stavely's office. She was glad the other woman couldn't see her as she knocked tentatively at Lawson's door, and while waiting for his, 'Come in,' straightened the skirt of her second best suit. Its jacket was on its hanger in her own room, and it seemed much too formal to put the jacket on with Mrs Stavely watching, only to take it off again when she returned to her typing. Her skirt was brown as was her closely fitting jersey shirt. She had felt good when she'd set out this morning, and hoped her skirt hadn't seated as she obeyed Lawson's summons to go in.

'No need to knock every time you want to come in,' he told her without looking up from what he was doing.

How did he know it was her? she wondered briefly, before common sense told her Mrs Stavely wouldn't have let any unexpected visitor past her door. Just then Lawson looked up. She'd had her little speech already prepared, but as his dark eyes looked and held hers, everything went temporarily out of her head.

'I—er—came to see you,' she began, 'because . . .' She stopped at his suddenly sharp look.

'If you've come to tell me you want to go back to Statistics, you can forget it,' he told her, his voice sounding hard and uncompromising.

'Why should I want . . .' she began, then as light dawned that he thought she couldn't stand the pace of working for him, her head came up. 'I'll admit everything up here still seems a bit muddled to me at the moment,' she said, trying not to get heated, 'but I wouldn't dream of asking for my old job back.'

Lawson eyed her for a moment, then as if realising only then that she was still standing, he invited her to take the chair she had used at her interview with him.

'You enjoy what you've been doing so far?'

'I find it challenging and rewarding,' Ivory told him honestly.

'You were wasted working for Mr Fletcher,' he said, without making it sound like a compliment. He put down the fountain pen he had been using and leaned back in his chair. 'Everything will straighten itself out in time—don't let yourself become over-anxious about anything. Feel free to ask either Mrs Stavely or myself about anything you don't understand,' he told her, and she couldn't help the sudden thought that he could be quite kind when he wasn't being unbearable.

'Thank you,' she said quietly. Then realising that wasn't the point of why she was here, and knowing he would be enquiring any moment if she wasn't in his office to ask for a transfer, then what was the purpose of her visit, she stated baldly, 'Jan asked me to give you a message.'

'Jan—You've seen him?'

That sharp look was back in his eyes. She decided to disregard it; it would soon disappear when she told him about the book Jan said he was keen to have.

'No, I haven't seen him,' she said, striving for some of Mrs Stavely's unflappability. 'He telephoned me on Friday . . .'

'From Holland?'

'Yes, from Holland.' She knew she was in danger of flaring up and wished he would let her get on with it without asking all these questions.

'Did he say when he would be coming over?'

'Shortly, he said.'

'I see—and no doubt you'll be seeing him again?'

'Have you any objection?' she asked tightly, knowing that at any second she was going to blow it.

'My dear Miss Dutton, you can do what the hell you like—it's no concern of mine. Provided,' he added as an afterthought, 'the results of your staying out half the night don't have an adverse effect on the smooth running of this office.' Ivory was on her feet when his next sarcastic comment reached her ears. 'I wouldn't want to make a habit of taking you home with a bad head.'

'I never asked you to in the first place,' she stormed back, her control broken. 'It was you who insisted I go home—I was quite content to stay on until five.'

She was too angry to notice a look that might have been admiration pass over his face as he noted the sparks of anger flashing from her eyes.

'If I remember rightly, you could barely keep your head up, it was aching so badly,' he said smoothly, which annoyed her even more that he could be so calm when she was so furious. 'I couldn't humanely do anything other than take you home.'

She almost spat the words 'Humane, huh!' at him, before realising that by becoming angry she had lost any ground she might have had. Resorting to a slanging match, she decided, was beneath her. Without so much as looking at him again, she turned on her heel and marched to the door.

'I believe you said you had a message for me,' his calm voice stopped her. Then her mind almost blanked completely at his next words, 'You know, Ivory, you really are a striking creature when you're angry.'

She ignored him. 'Jan has the book you wanted,' she

stated bluntly, her lips coming firmly together to stop herself from adding anything else. His look didn't tell her anything—if he was pleased with the message from Jan, she'd never know it.

By the end of the week, Ivory was beginning to get an insight into the job she had taken over, and by the end of her third week everything had fallen into place. The door between her office and that of Mrs Stavely now stayed closed, there being no need for her to keep nipping in with every query she came across. For the most part she was able to sort out the answers for herself. She was kept too busy to feel any isolation at being in an office all by herself and since a steady trickle of visitors made their way up to the top floor, she was forced many times to break off from her work.

She had been working directly for Lawson for four weeks when Mrs Stavely told her Jenny had had her baby. 'It was premature,' she said, 'but they're both all right. It's a little boy.' A soft look came over her face which transferred itself to Ivory as they talked babies. They were in Mrs Stavely's office and Ivory didn't hear Lawson come out of his room and stand watching her for a moment.

'If I might interrupt the gooey talk, perhaps you can tell me where you put the Amalgamated Copper file?' he broke in on them.

Ivory caught the faintly sardonic look he favoured her with, but stood her ground and refused to scuttle back to her own office as she had been prone to do rather than risk any sort of exchange with him. For it seemed they were like pieces of flint rubbing against each other, and they had had more than one tight-lipped exchange since she had worked for him. Mrs Stavely, though, didn't seem to notice the sardonic look of him, and handed him the file with a smile in her voice.

'I was just telling Ivory the good news about Jenny and the baby both being fit and well, and Ivory was saying she wouldn't mind what sex her baby was so long as it was healthy.'

Ivory knew she was blushing, and wished she had gone back to her office now, as Lawson gave her a look that clearly said, 'Fancy that—and you never told me!'

'We were talking hypothetically,' she muttered defensively.

'Naturally,' drawled Lawson, his expression taking on a teasing light for the first time.

But that word 'naturally' hurt. It was as though it was obvious to all that she would never lose the control she had over her sexual emotions. Feeling choked suddenly, she did a prompt about-turn and went quickly back into her own office.

She had no idea Lawson had followed her, had witnessed the mist of tears she was trying rapidly to blink back, until he said gently: 'Care to tell me what I said that's made you come over all weepy?' with a surprisingly gentle note in his voice.

Ivory pulled herself together as best she could. 'No!' she snapped, making her voice deliberately sharp, for only by getting her aggression going could she save herself from bursting into tears.

She expected him to be offended by her tone, but disconcertingly he wasn't. 'If you won't tell me, you won't,' he shrugged, taking the sheet of paper she would have rolled into her typewriter out of her hands. 'But don't tear yourself to pieces about whatever it was—you know I wouldn't intentionally hurt you. Now pop down to the canteen for ten minutes.' The gentle note in his voice faded as a teasing note entered. 'I believe you ladies think tea is the panacea for all ills.'

Not sure her voice was up to arguing the point, and since he looked as if he had no intention whatsoever of leaving until she had obeyed his instruction, Ivory picked up her bag and went.

What a strange man he was, she thought as she sipped her tea. She had just witnessed in him an unexpected sensitivity. Many men wouldn't even have noticed she was upset. Lawson had accepted too without argument that she couldn't tell him what had upset her. A fine fool I should have looked, she thought, coming round rapidly, telling him his carelessly spoken, 'Naturally' had triggered off thoughts she had believed no longer bothered her.

Bothered wasn't quite the right word, she reasoned; other girls she knew made no secret of the fact they slept around—but that wasn't her. But it hadn't *bothered* her, she had always thought physical love would come when the time was right, and by right, in her book it meant marriage. That was, she qualified, until Michael had made such a big issue of it—only then had she begun to doubt that she was in any way different from anyone else. And Lawson's 'Naturally' had made it seem as if she had a giant-sized notice pinned to her saying, 'Untouchable'.

Lawson was nowhere in evidence when she returned to her office. If possible she hoped she could finish off the day without coming into contact with him again. Her good fairy must have been with her, she thought, as she went home that night, for on taking some papers through to Mrs Stavely, she learned that Lawson had gone out and would not be returning that day.

Glad that it was again Friday and she had two whole days in which to recharge her batteries before work again on

Monday, Ivory said goodbye to Mandy who was going to visit Adrian's parents for the weekend, and went into the bathroom with the intention of washing her hair. But before she could so much as turn on the taps, the front door bell pealed. Wondering who it could be, she tripped lightly down the two flights of stairs, and opening the door found Jan on the other side.

'You don't mind that I visit you without making a prior arrangement?' he asked, which was his polite way she realised, of asking if it was convenient to call.

'No—No, of course not,' Ivory smiled at him. 'Come in.'

Back in the flat, the door closed to the outside world, Jan looked at her, his pleasure on seeing her again evident. 'You are as lovely as I remembered you,' he told her, causing her to think he must be flattering her, for she had scrubbed her face free of the small amount of make-up she used when she'd arrived home, was wearing her oldest jeans and if he'd timed his arrival two minutes later, she would have had her head in the wash basin. 'I should have telephoned you, I know,' he told her, smiling at her confusion at his compliment. 'But this week has been one round of meetings and I wasn't sure I would be able to come to London tonight or whether I would have to wait until tomorrow—I was able to wind the meeting up around four today, and as you see, here I am.'

'You've only just arrived?' Ivory asked, not sure she was too happy that he had made the flat his first port of call. If that was what he had done, it showed every indication that he was very keen to see her. She wasn't sure she was yet ready for involvement of any kind.

'You don't mind that I come straight to see you?' Jan asked quietly, his smile fading making his face look so sombre, she didn't have the heart to voice any objection— she could be reading too much into it anyway.

'Of course not,' she said, forcing a smile, then changing the subject, 'If you didn't finish work until four and have flown here straightaway, you can't have had anything to eat. Can I get you some . . .'

'I was rather hoping you would come out with me for a meal?'

If Jan had had his way, she would have spent all Saturday and Sunday with him, and much though she enjoyed being in his company, the pang of unease she had felt at his seeming eagerness to be with her on Friday made her tell him she couldn't see him until the evenings. When he took her home on Saturday evening, he repeated his invitation to spend the following day with him.

'Are you sure you won't come with me tomorrow—we could spend the day in the country or do anything else that appeals to you?'

'I'm sorry, Jan,' she said, feeling mean but unable to give in, 'I have several things crying out for my attention tomorrow. Can we leave it as we arranged—I'll see you about seven in the evening?'

'If that is what you wish,' said Jan, his eyes crinkling at the corners as he in turn attempted to take the sombre expression away from her face. 'Lawson knows I'm in London—I shall just have to take up his invitation to join him for lunch tomorrow.'

Ivory was ready when Jan called for her the next evening, and remembering he had said he would be lunching with Lawson, decided she wouldn't stay out very late with him. There was every likelihood that he might have told Lawson that he had seen her this weekend, and she wasn't looking forward to any of Lawson's acid if she had a repeat of that ghastly headache she'd had the last time she'd dated Jan three times in a row.

Accordingly, after the meal they shared in the candlelit

atmosphere of a very smart hotel, she asked him if he had any objection if they left.

'You are tired?'

'No, it isn't that—and I don't mean to be rude, because I have enjoyed this evening tremendously. It's just that I'm a working girl, and I want to be bright-eyed in the morning.' And because she had a feeling of guilt about what she had just said and in view of the fact that Jan had taken the trouble to take her out the last three nights—forgetting completely he had asked her out for the very obvious reason that that was what he wanted to do—she felt obliged to explain the adverse effect the previous late nights had on her.

'And you say Lawson took you home from your office?' Jan questioned when she had lightly told him she couldn't expect Lawson to take her home if the same thing happened again.

'Yes, that's right. It was very good of him.' It choked her to say it—but, she realised, it was the truth.

'Then that explains his remark to me this afternoon.'

'Remark?'

'I told Lawson you were dining with me this evening—his face was very serious when he told me I was to look after you.'

Lawson's remark to Jan gave her some food for thought as Jan drove her home. His face had been serious, Jan had said, when he had told him to look after her. Now why had he told him to do that? It was an odd remark to make—almost as if he considered himself her guardian, warning her escort to see she came to no harm. She shrugged all thoughts of Lawson away as Jan pulled up outside her flat. Lawson was just looking after his own interests, she decided—she'd be useless to him in the morning if she wasn't fit to cope with her job.

Jan came with her up the stairs to the door of her flat, but there he stopped. 'Since you have said you don't want to be up late, I won't ask you if I can come in,' he told her. 'I am going back to Holland in the morning.' Ivory felt his arms come round her—she'd told him 'No' the last time he had intimated he was going to kiss her, but she should have known if she'd thought about it that their friendship couldn't stay static for very much longer.

Perhaps it was because he had already told her he did not intend going inside her flat that she relaxed more than she might otherwise have done. When his head came down she didn't turn her head away, but waited for the feel of his mouth over her own. His kiss was nothing like the one Lawson had bestowed on her, she thought, feeling uneasy that Lawson should enter her head when all her thoughts should be centred on the man who now held her in his arms. It was no good; much as she liked Jan, was fond of him even, she just wasn't enjoying being kissed by him. She stirred in his arms, and instantly he let her go.

But she wasn't prepared for the very warm look in his eyes, or for the huskily whispered, 'My lovely Ivory!' She looked away from him, finding it impossible to hold his look, and heard him say softly, 'I will go now, my dear, otherwise you will not have your early night after all.'

Ivory awoke the following morning feeling anything but bright-eyed. Oh she had had her early night, but had worried so much about the way she and Jan had parted that her sleep had only been fitful. Over and over again she heard the tender note in his voice as he'd called her 'my dear'. She couldn't honestly believe that the wealthy diamond merchant Jan was could be falling for her. It was impossible—yet all the signs were there. And as though that wasn't enough to upset her, she couldn't help but remember she had actually thought of Lawson Alexander when she had been in Jan's arms.

Sighing, she got out of bed and pattered to the kitchen. 'Hi,' said Mandy, rescuing burning toast from under the grill. 'What are you doing up this early?—You haven't got a train to catch. Want some toast?'

'I'll do it—I expect you're in a hurry,' Ivory answered. 'How did you get on with Adrian's parents?'

'His father's a darling, but for his mother read—dragon!'

Ivory popped a couple of pieces of bread under the grill and turned to look at Mandy. She sounded quite light-hearted, so if she was serious about Adrian, his mother hadn't managed to put her off, if her cheerful expression was anything to go by.

'You don't look so chirpy,' Mandy observed. 'Your eyes look tired—don't tell me you spent the whole weekend reading? Honestly, Ivory . . .'

'Jan arrived on Friday after you'd gone—I went out to dinner with him three times.' She turned back to the toast which was as good as an excuse as any to hide the disquiet she was feeling from Mandy's sharp eyes.

'Serious, is it?' Mandy asked casually.

'No.' There was much more she could have added, and she thought she could have confided in Mandy—but there was no time now. Perhaps tonight if Mandy wasn't going out. Mandy was quite levelheaded when it came down to it —she would tell her if she was imagining it or not.

Arriving at the office a few minutes before nine, Ivory just had sufficient time to hang up her coat and slip her handbag into her desk drawer, when the intercom on her desk buzzed. Flicking her eyes downwards, she saw it was Lawson calling her and without pausing to wonder how he knew she had arrived, she had flicked the switch and before she could say anything was being told shortly to, 'Come in, please.'

He cut off before she could answer him in any way. It was

going to be one of those days, she thought, picking up a
notepad and pencil. She didn't often take down his dictation—but luckily her head was clear even though, according to Mandy, her eyes looked tired.

She went through Mrs Stavely's office. She hadn't even
had time to come in and wish her her usual good morning,
Lawson had been so quick off the mark. Mrs Stavely was
busy opening the post Ivory knew would have been ad-
dressed directly to Lawson. She looked up answering
Ivory's greeting.

'Mr Alexander wants me to go in,' Ivory explained.

'I know.' Something in Mrs Stavely's voice warned her
Lawson wasn't in the best of tempers, but she was too good
a secretary to give more away as Ivory paused beside her
desk for a moment, save to say, 'I wouldn't keep him
waiting if I were you.'

Knowing Lawson was disturbing when he was in a good
mood, and wondering how she would fare with him in a bad
mood, Ivory opened his door.

He had already opened his mail marked Private, but
looked up from what he was reading as she came into the
room, motioning her to the chair it was now usual for her to
sit in. Conscious of his eyes on her as she crossed the thickly
carpeted room, she tried for a cool efficient manner and sat
down, smoothing her grey skirt down over her knees as she
did so. Then, pencil poised over her notepad, she looked at
him indicating she was ready to start.

His glance passed briefly over her face before his eyes
turned to the letter in his hand, where she thought he had
begun to read again. 'Been painting the town red again, I
see,' he said shortly, putting the letter down on the blotter
before him.

'I . . .' She almost fell into the trap. If he was in a foul mood, and wanted to have a go at someone, he wasn't going to use her as a target. She swallowed her immediate ire, and said calmly, 'You could say that—though you'll be pleased to know I don't have a headache.'

All she got for her pains was a grunt, which told her nothing, and since he seemed in no hurry to start, she forced herself to sit quietly until he was ready. She hoped her nerves would stand up to his rapid dictation—some of his edginess was transmitting itself to her.

How long she sat there, pencil poised, she had no idea. But when she turned her head to flick a glance at him, it was to see he wasn't reading the rest of his mail as she had supposed, but was looking directly at her with every appearance of being in no hurry to look away.

'Did you want me to take dictation?' It was out before she could stop it, as the calm she had exerted before surrendered to her quick tongue.

'As a matter of fact, no.'

It was a cool calm statement to which there was no answer, and she was left wondering if he hadn't called her in to take down his dictation—then what on earth had he called her in for?

CHAPTER SEVEN

WHEN Lawson did deign to tell her what he had called her in for, Ivory had the hardest job in the world trying to keep her equilibrium—she didn't think she managed very well.

'It seems,' he said, his eyes now fully on her, 'that all hell has broken loose at the Manchester works—I dispatched Harrington there last week to deal with it.' She knew Brian Harrington was Lawson's chief trouble-shooter, but kept quiet as he went on. 'Harrington appears to have muffed it, and though I can barely spare the time with the take over of Talbot and Blair going through, the only way to try and stave off industrial action is for me to go to Manchester personally.'

Ivory's mind grasped that things must be bad if the usually trouble-free Manchester branch were talking of strike action. She could see too that it would help if the head of Alexander's went to Manchester and showed his employees he cared enough to go and talk to them personally —but what he was asking of her she couldn't see. She had hoped he knew enough about her work to know she would do all she could to help Mrs Stavely keep this end running smoothly, though his team of Management were well versed in how he wanted things running in his absence—his frequent trips abroad bore witness to that.

'What is it exactly you want me to do?' she asked at last, her brain refusing to come up with any answer.

'Didn't I say?' he asked as though in surprise that he had overlooked to mention her role in this crisis, for all she was sure he knew he hadn't so much as given her a clue. 'I shall want you with me, of course.'

'Me?' she ejaculated.

Lawson looked at her steadily for a few seconds. If she didn't already know he was in a foul mood, she would have believed he was actually enjoying this moment.

'You,' he said deliberately.

'Why me?' she argued. 'Why not Mrs Stavely? She'd . . .' She stopped right there. Lawson she saw, as his mouth tightened, was not in a mood to be argued with.

'Just to put the record straight,' he told her shortly, 'Mrs Stavely has a semi-invalid husband and couldn't go with me in any case.'

Some of the heat went out of Ivory. She had worked closely with Mrs Stavely for a whole month and hadn't found that out—it made her feel guilty even though since Mrs Stavely never mentioned her husband she had thought her a widow, and hadn't liked to ask about him for fear of upsetting her.

'Mrs Stavely doesn't like talking about her personal life,' Lawson told her, which helped her to feel less guilty, though she was sure that wasn't the reason he told her. 'Whether Mrs Stavely could go with me or not is beside the point—it's not Mrs Stavely I want with me, but you.' He was still tight-lipped and Ivory was forced to bite back the challenging 'Why?' that sprang to her lips—she had an idea she would know soon enough.

She had reckoned, though, without Lawson's shrewd ability to read her mind. 'What's your objection to going?' he asked. 'I'm sure your personal life won't suffer—Jan went back this morning, didn't he?'

Swallowing hard, she determined not to get riled. Her personal life was no concern of his. And he already knew

Jan was going back this morning, she was sure, without her having to confirm it.

'What time do we start out for Manchester?' she asked.

If she thought to take him out of his stride by ignoring his question, she found herself very much mistaken, for suddenly he became totally businesslike, telling her they ought to be on their way as soon as possible, but that he would have to clear up a few things this end first.

'You'd better go home and pack—I'll come round for you about twelve.'

Having accepted it was a waste of time arguing with him, she stood up from her chair. 'How long will we be away?' she asked, which she thought was a reasonable enough question.

'I've no idea.' He was already immersed in the correspondence in front of him. 'You'd better ring up and book the accommodation.'

The hotel would want to know how long they were staying, she thought, but since the expression on his face told her he was no longer with her, but deep into whatever immediate problem was before him, she realised she would only annoy him further by pointing this out to him.

Mrs Stavely told her the name of the hotel Lawson usually stayed in when he was in Manchester, and seeing Mrs Stavely looked extremely busy, Ivory went to her own office and was soon making the call. Since Lawson had occupied a suite of rooms in Amsterdam, she supposed he would want the same this trip—but she knew, the mood he was in, he wouldn't take kindly to her interrupting him to find out.

Having got through to the hotel and made her initial enquiry, Ivory waited for the receptionist to return. It seemed from what the girl had said before asking her pleasantly to hold on for a moment that everyone had chosen that week to hold conferences in Manchester. She hoped she wouldn't have any trouble making the booking—that would be the last straw as far as Lawson was concerned.

As she waited for the receptionist to come back, she turned her thoughts away from Lawson and his impending displeasure, concentrating instead on what she would take with her. She wasn't going to be caught out again the way she had been in Amsterdam. Should she take a long dress? Oh, help—what if Lawson insisted she dine with him again —would he again threaten to dismiss her if she started to refuse?

'Two bedrooms, you said?'

The receptionist was back again, and Ivory came back quickly to confirm, 'Yes, that's right,' relief flooding through her that she'd been able to make the booking. 'I'm not sure how long we'll be staying.'

That was one hurdle out of the way—now she'd better get home; it wouldn't do not to be ready when Lawson called for her. Though she couldn't help but enquire from Mrs Stavely if there was anything she could do before she left.

'No, thank you, Ivory.' For all she was busy Mrs Stavely managed to retain her unflappable air, Ivory noted with admiration. 'Things will quieten down this afternoon—if I'm pushed I can always send the less important stuff down to the typing pool.'

Ivory couldn't see her doing that, but it salved her conscience somewhat that in an emergency there was always that avenue Mrs Stavely could use.

It took her very little time to pack. She took care of her clothes and had pressed one of the suits she was taking with her only yesterday. For the journey she changed into her off-white trouser suit—not a very sensible colour, she had to admit, but it was washable, so there was no problem there.

It fitted her well, she thought, as she surveyed herself in the mirror, showing up her long length of leg, its short jacket coming to just below her waist.

Had Lawson kept to the time he said he would call she would have been downstairs with her suitcase ready and waiting for him. But when a knock sounded on her door at twenty to the hour, she looked out of the window and saw Lawson's Aston Martin was parked outside. Mr Phillips on the ground floor must have let him in, she realised as she went to open the door.

'Come in,' she invited Lawson, thinking he must have broken all records to clear up the mound of paper work on his desk. 'I'm almost ready except for writing a note for Mandy.'

Her heart-to-heart with her flatmate about Jan would have to wait until she arrived back, she thought, and she was pleased that maybe because of this trip to Manchester coming when it had, her anxieties about Jan no longer seemed to loom as large as they had last night.

Lawson seemed to dominate the room, she thought, as she came back into the sitting room after leaving her note for Mandy on the kitchen table. His eyes flicked over her as she came towards him, taking in the look of her in her nifty trouser suit.

'All set?' he asked, reaching for her suitcase.

Some of his irritability seemed to have left him, she was pleased to see. She even thought she saw a glimmer of amusement cross his face as he noted the size of her suitcase —but it didn't break into a smile. She had to admit she had packed more than she thought she would need, and guessed he knew she had no intention of being caught out again.

They had been travelling for some time before Lawson made any effort to talk to her. Ivory assumed he was either concentrating on his driving, for the car was travelling at a fair speed along the motorway, either that or his mind was on the situation he had to deal with when they arrived at their destination.

'We'll turn off at the next junction and find somewhere to eat—I expect you could do with a bite of something.'

She was starving if the truth were known, but wasn't likely to tell him so. If he'd decided to drive straight to Manchester without stopping she would have kept quiet, and hoped her stomach would do the same.

A few miles off the motorway, he pulled up at a wayside pub. Since it was on a minor road, she assumed he had sorted this place out on one of his many previous visits.

The meal they had was well cooked and plentiful without being pretentious. Good home-cooked plain fare, her mother would have called it. Lawson allowed them ten minutes to drink their coffee while he smoked one of the cheroots he favoured. Since this was, she supposed, a business lunch, Lawson outlined what would be expected of her. She discovered she was there very much as a secretary and would be spending her time taking down his dictation and typing it back.

'Won't I be coming to any of the meetings with you?'

'I prefer you with your hair straight the way it is,' he told her, explaining, 'some of the language at the type of meeting in front of me would make your hair curl.'

'Oh,' she said, before thinking for a minute. 'I'm not such a shrinking violet as all that, you know—I am aware, I think, that the air can sometimes get a little blue when tempers become frayed.'

'I think purple would be a better colour to describe what will be going on if the chief trouble-stirrer is the chap I think it is,' he told her, then paused, no humour at all in his expression as he challenged her, 'Are you telling me you've come out of your emotional shell?'

Her eyes grew wide as she stared at him. Was he asking her what she thought he was asking her? She could tell nothing from his expression, yet the air seemed suddenly charged as he waited for her answer.

'Do you mean . . .' she began—he couldn't possibly be meaning that, she thought, utterly shaken to think he could be asking her if she had been to bed with Jan. 'You can't possibly be asking . . .' Of course he couldn't, her reason told her—she was misunderstanding him in some way. Yet as his eyes refused to let go the hold they had on hers, she knew positively that that *was* what he was asking, and somehow she had the absurd idea he was waiting tensely for her answer.

'I'm no different now from the person I was in Amsterdam,' she told him coldly. And as the cheroot he was holding between his fingers snapped in two and was dumped into the ash tray, she got up and left him.

In the ladies' room she fumed against him. Who did he think he was to ask such a question? But more importantly the thought that came to override her anger at his colossal nerve was the memory that he had referred to her as being in an 'emotional shell'.

He was standing outside the car waiting for her when she came out. She gave him a fleeting look, then ignored him completely as he held the door open for her. She couldn't even offer him a thank you, she was so uptight.

She expected at the very least some sort of apology as they again started on their way, for he must know he had upset her, but his next words were far from an apology—if anything, it seemed he had audacity enough to pursue the subject.

'Still pining for Michael?' he asked.

She had forgotten he knew about Michael, and was flabbergasted as much by his cheek as the fact that he had remembered his name.

'Who's Michael?' she said airily, and looked determinedly out of the side window. She doubted Lawson would allow her to leave it there, but surprisingly he did, and there was very little conversation between them after that, then he was drawing up outside their hotel.

Feeling in no way friendly towards him, she trotted beside him, preceding him only when he stood back to allow her to go before him into the hotel. Then he was striding to the desk, and determined not to race after him like some well trained performing animal, Ivory slowed down to her own pace, gazing about her and in no mood to hurry to his side. She reached the desk as he was taking possession of their keys after signing in.

'Come on,' he said shortly, picking up both their cases.

About to argue shouldn't she sign in as well, she was forced after all to trot after him as he reached the lift first and held it open for her to get in. When the lift stopped he strode with his long easy stride away from her, and since he still had her suitcase, there was nothing she could do but follow him. He really was the most arrogant, ruthless brute, she thought, catching up with him when he stopped outside one of the several doors along the corridor.

'May I have my room key?' she asked, as the door opened and he went in, taking her luggage with him.

He ignored her and there was nothing for it but to join him in the sitting room of his suite. She'd better calm down and see if he had any instructions for her, she supposed, but when he continued to look at her, a self-satisfied smile on his face, she could hold on to her temper no longer.

'If it isn't too much trouble, do you think I could have the key to my room?' she said, hoping sarcasm would cover the fact that she was almost shaking with temper.

Lawson pointed to the two doors going in opposite directions to each other. 'Take your pick,' he said loftily.

Ivory glanced quickly from one closed door to the other, then back at him. 'What do you mean?' she asked, feeling an ominous prickling at the nape of her neck.

'I mean, Miss Dutton,' Lawson replied suavely, making no attempt to hide his sarcasm, 'that when I asked you to arrange the accommodation, I had no idea you would have a more personal arrangement in mind than I had.'

'P-personal arrangement?' she was fairly spluttering.

'I had thought you might arrange to sleep some way away from me,' Lawson told her coolly. 'If not on another floor I thought you would at least be at the far end of the corridor away from me. But it appears I was in error. Contrary to my belief that you can't stand the sight of me, you've booked a suite to include two bedrooms.'

She ignored his sarcasm as the realisation of what must have happened crowded in on her. She didn't even feel the the annoyance she would otherwise have done at the way he was making out she had booked the two-bedroomed suite on purpose. He must know that just wasn't true.

'It's a mistake,' she said abruptly. 'I'll go and change it.' She would have taken off then, but the hand Lawson placed on her shoulder stayed her.

'They're fully booked,' he said. 'I enquired when only one key and its duplicate came across the desk.'

'But . . .'

'Don't fret about it,' Lawson said easily, dropping his hand away from her shoulder. 'I daresay my reputation can stand it.'

'Your reputation?' Ivory asked, blinking rapidly at the

arrogance of the man. He made no mention of her reputation. Then knowing she would get nowhere going along
that tack, 'Are you sure there are no more rooms available?'

She didn't like the way Lawson's eyes narrowed at her
questioning what he had told her, but managed not to look
away as he said shortly:

'What's the matter—do you think I have designs on your
virtue? You've stayed the night with me in much closer
association before,' he reminded her, 'and you came to no
harm then.'

She didn't like being reminded of that occasion. And if
he'd care to cast his own memory back he would remember
he hadn't known she was in the other bed until it was time
to get up.

As if tiring of the whole debate, Lawson went to push
both bedroom doors open, signalling that he was not going
to argue further. 'It will suit me very well if I want you in a
hurry to have you near at hand.' His tone had changed and
he was all no-nonsense now. 'Make your mind up which
room you want—I want to change before I go to the works.'

'T-the one on the left,' Ivory told him not at all
bothered which room she had, but saying the first thing that
came into her head since it now appeared he was pressed for
time.

She didn't see him again before he returned from the
works. Having dumped her case in her room, he left her
standing in the middle of the sitting room, going to his own
room and shutting the door with a decisive click. Ivory went
to the room she had chosen, closing the door quietly. If ever
there was another time she was called upon to accompany
him, she decided, she'd make doubly sure her room was as
far away from his as possible—preferably in another hotel.

Determined not to be in the sitting room when he came
out of his bedroom, she set about her unpacking. She was

glad she hadn't brought the pink dress with her, electing instead to bring a full-length dress of midnight blue silk jersey, that went well with her honey-blonde hair and fair complexion. It was suitable for dinner, she thought, without being formal.

She had barely finished her unpacking when she heard a movement in the sitting room, which was followed by the sound of the outer door closing. In no hurry to investigate his departure, she finished what she was doing and left her room only when a knock sounded on the outer door.

Answering the door, she saw one of the hotel porters weighted down with a typewriter. 'In here,' she said quickly, opening the door wide as the little man looked ready to drop it. Her eyes hurriedly scanned the room and she saw that besides a couple of easy chairs and occasional tables, there was a large table beneath the window. 'Would you put it over there, please,' she requested. After he had gone she looked at the workmanlike machine, he had brought in, reflecting that none of the hotel staff could be under any illusion that this was anything but a working trip.

She went over to get a closer look at the typewriter. It was a fairly new model of a type she had used before. Lawson must have left instructions for it to be delivered on his way out, she guessed, feeling unexpectedly restless. She had no idea what time he would be back, but hoped he wouldn't expect her to sit around twiddling her thumbs.

Rebellion hit her at the very idea—and without thinking further, she decided to leave the room and take a look around the hotel. She didn't get much further than the lounge, for seeing there were several people there, most of them it seemed sitting with a tray of tea in front of them, it came to her that she was not a little thirsty herself.

A passing waiter seeing her hesitating asked if he could help, and in no time she herself was seated with a tray of tea before her. On the point of sipping her tea, she almost dropped her cup when the last voice she expected to hear said incredulously, 'Ivory—Ivory Dutton! Fancy seeing you here!' She looked up and saw that the man she had thought had broken her heart some eight months ago was standing looking down at her as if she had appeared by some conjuring trick.

'Why, Michael!' she gasped her own surprise, and before it had properly registered that joyfully, happily, she was completely free from those painful emotion-tearing thoughts about him, he had taken the seat beside her.

'What are you doing here?' Michael was the first to recover from the surprise. 'I lost track of you when you left Luton.'

'I'm here with my boss—I'm a secretary with a London firm now.'

'I heard you'd gone to live in London.'

There was a short uncomfortable silence. She had no idea what Michael expected her to say in answer to that, and momentarily speech was taken away from her as she looked at him and realised for the first time what cold, pale blue eyes he had. She had thought for some time she was over him, but a doubt had remained that she wouldn't know for sure until she saw him again. But now she knew, and as a wave of gladness washed over her she found her voice and asked what he was doing in Manchester.

'It's our annual sales meeting, we're congregating here from all over the country,' he told her, his eyes making a thorough study of her face and figure. 'You haven't changed any, Ivory—you're still as beautiful as ever you were.'

Ivory chose to ignore that statement—there seemed no point to it. Instead she asked him about his work and discovered he was doing very well in his job. He was sales manager, as she already knew, and according to Michael he was being groomed for bigger and better things. She had never realised before that he was such a company man—whenever he had talked about his work before she had always been eager to listen, but now, as he seemed to go on and on, she found her interest sadly lacking, and had to force herself to maintain a polite interest until at last Michael himself seemed to realise he had been doing most of the talking.

'I seem to be going on a bit,' he said at length. 'Tell me what you've been doing just lately?' Then not waiting for her answer, 'Do you often go on business trips with your boss?'

'Not very often.'

'How long are you here for?' he asked, and again before she could answer, 'You won't be working tonight, will you? How about having dinner with me . . .?' He paused, causing her to wonder what was in his mind. 'Or perhaps you'd rather not . . .' he said slowly.

Ivory guessed then what his pause had been all about. He thought she was still in love with him. It annoyed her that he could think she could still be in love with him, so much so that uncaring if Lawson had any work for her or not, she sent Michael a friendly smile and told him, 'I'd like very much to have dinner with you, Michael,' and if she hadn't convinced him by the time the meal was over that he meant nothing to her any more, then he was more conceited than she was only just beginning to realise he really was.

She parted from Michael after having agreed to meet him at .eight-thirty, and returned to the suite. If Lawson had been trying to get her on the phone the hotel would have taken a message, she reasoned. But when she lifted the phone in her room to enquire, she was told there were no messages for her.

When there was no sign of Lawson at seven o'clock, Ivory gave up waiting for him. He had probably arranged to have dinner with Brian Harrington before he'd set out from London, she decided. The two men would have to meet to discuss what had led up to the dispute. Well, if he didn't have the courtesy to ring through and let her know what was happening, then she wasn't going to go without her dinner until such time as he remembered he had brought a secretary with him.

Ivory was bathed and dressed in her midnight blue dress at a quarter to eight. She had spent a few minutes making up her eyes and applying a film of pink lipstick to her mouth, and felt without conceit that Michael could have no complaint with the finished picture.

Deciding to wait until nearer the appointed time in the sitting room, she opened her bedroom door and was startled to see the long, lean shape of Lawson Alexander unfolding himself from his chair. It was a shock seeing him when she hadn't even heard him come in, but she managed to stay outwardly calm as she watched him carefully taking in everything about her appearance. Her dress had a snugly fitting bodice, and she saw his eyes flicker from her face to rest briefly on her breasts before moving on to take in the rest of her.

'Thinking of going somewhere?' he asked at last, his very tone telling her he knew she hadn't dressed up to go to dinner with him.

'I met—an old friend while I was in the lounge. I'm having dinner with him.'

She watched as if mesmerised as Lawson shook his head slowly from side to side. 'Not so,' he said coolly. 'You and I have work to do.'

'But I've already made arrangements . . .' she began. It

didn't matter a row of beans to her whether she dined with Michael or not, but she felt bound to protest. Lawson should have warned her before he went out that she would be working that night.

'Then you'd better cancel your arrangements, hadn't you?'

Ivory gave him a speaking look, and without saying another word turned from him and stormed to her room. She hated it when he used those sardonic tones on her, she fumed, as she stood in her room knowing she would have to do as he had ordered.

There was over half an hour to go before she was due to meet Michael—she wasn't in any hurry to ring him. She wasn't in any hurry to change either, she decided, taking off her dress and sitting on the bed in her petticoat. She'd waited long enough for Lawson Alexander—now let him wait for her! She railed against him for the next five minutes, then decided she'd better phone Michael. Since she had told him she would meet him in the lounge where they had parted earlier, he could well take it into his head to be there early and sip a drink of some kind until she arrived.

Getting up from the bed, she picked up the phone and asked to be put through to Mr Michael Stephens' room, and in no time was hearing his voice saying, 'Hello.'

'Oh, Michael—Ivory here,' she said easily, glorying in the fact the sound of his voice no longer had the power to upset her. 'I'm sorry to ring you so late, but I'm afraid I can't manage to meet you for dinner after all.'

'Can't meet me?' Michael questioned. It was almost as if he thought it impossible that she had anything other to do than pass her time with him, she thought, not liking anything about his voice, particularly the sulky tone he was using.

'I'm sorry, Michael, I've only just discovered I have some work to do.'

Michael hadn't been very pleased she thought as she replaced the receiver, and stood in silent thought for a moment or two. Then her whole spine stiffened, for thinking she was in the room by herself, she distinctly heard a sound.

She whipped round, her eyes wide as scarlet colour flooded her cheeks. For there, leaning negligently against the open door, stood Lawson Alexander. The look on his face could only be called derisory, as he surveyed her from top to toe as she stood, her face crimson, clad only in her petticoat, before him.

'Is it too much for me to expect a little privacy?' she flared, sparks flying from her lovely eyes at the cheek of him to calmly open her door and stand there until she had finished her phone call. She wasn't quite sure what made her more angry—the fact that he must have listened to every word of her phone call, or the fact that she suddenly felt defenceless dressed as she was only in her underwear.

'I take it Michael was the *friend* you met in the lounge,' Lawson commented, letting her see the cause for his derisory look, and seeming to have no intention of moving. 'I would have thought you'd have had more pride than to let him take up from where he left off.'

His voice sounded hard, and only then did she notice an answering glint of anger in his eyes, and realised that if she was angry, Lawson was absolutely flaming. Though why, she didn't have chance to sort out, just then.

'It's nothing to do with you whether I choose to let him take up from where he left off or not,' she told him shortly, wishing she could get to her robe which was hanging on the back of the door. But she was going nowhere near Lawson to get it with him in this mood—he looked set to break her in two. She heard him suck in his breath, and thought he was going to take a step nearer. 'Though if it's of any interest to you,' she qualified, not knowing why she should but suddenly afraid of the blaze in his eyes at her telling him it was nothing to do with him, 'I was merely going out with Michael tonight to show him he has no power at all to affect me now.'

'Now?' Lawson picked up quickly, though she was glad to see some of the heat seemed to be leaving him. 'Are you saying that now Jan is on the scene you find you're no longer carrying a torch for this Michael chap?'

He was as sharp as a tack—she had to give him that, and because she didn't want to answer him, she turned her back on him. Lawson was sharp, admittedly, but in this instance his two and two didn't add up correctly. And the last thing she was going to tell Jan's very good friend was anything of her personal feelings for Jan.

If by turning her back she'd hoped Lawson would go away, she found herself very much mistaken. She held herself tense as after a moment of complete silence she heard him move, she knew his movement was towards her, and knew also the futility of ordering him out of her room.

'Are you in love with Jan?' he asked, and his hands came down firmly on her bare shoulders as he turned her round to face him.

Looking into his unfathomable dark eyes, that now seemed darker than ever, Ivory found herself lost for words. Then Lawson was hauling her close up to him, and asking, 'Or don't you know yet?' His head came nearer and she knew he was going to kiss her—but she didn't move. If his kiss was going to be the same as the one he had given her in Amsterdam, she knew she had nothing to fear.

But Lawson's kiss when his mouth reached hers was

nothing like the Amsterdam kiss. His mouth rested lightly against hers for a moment, then as his hands left her shoulders and he pulled her into the circle of his arms, the pressure of his lips increased, seeking and searching, and she felt her heart flutter up until she thought she would choke.

Trying to push him away was useless, she found. All she was achieving in her struggles as her fists beat against him, was to give him the very little encouragement he needed to remove his lips from her mouth, push the dainty straps down her naked arms, and trace butterfly kisses over her throat and shoulders.

Suddenly something was happening inside her she had never dreamed could happen—not with Lawson. And as his lips left her shoulder to return to her mouth, she felt an awakening in her that made her want to respond to him. Repudiating the feeling, she pushed at his chest, and as he broke his kiss and looked deeply into her eyes, she summoned up every ounce of will power.

'No,' she said clearly, and, 'No!' again, because she was horribly afraid he was going to ignore her—and suddenly, she was doubting her own strength to resist. 'No, Lawson— please stop this!'

She was not at all sure what emotion raged through her when Lawson let her go. She wanted it to be relief—it had to be. But she had to whip herself up to the anger that only minutes before had come quite naturally.

'If you have quite finished,' she said, only just managing to get the right cold effect she wanted in her voice.

'My dear Ivory, that was barely a beginning.'

She didn't like the sound of that—it had connotations of a threat, for all his tone was cool.

'I don't know what you hoped to achieve from that— that—performance,' she said coldly.

It was as though, she thought, as he reached for her robe and gave it into her hands, that having touched her once, he was making certain not to touch her again and so trigger off another reaction. Her own reactions were too bewildering for her to know what to make of them, as she took the bundled-up robe from him.

'Whether I hoped to achieve anything by *that performance* is neither here nor there,' Lawson told her coldly; his anger seemed gone completely now—if anything, he gave the impression of wanting to dissociate himself entirely from what had just happened. 'But one thing was achieved,' he said, and Ivory was left holding her breath in case he was about to tell her he knew she had wanted to respond to him. Her relief was abundant when he added 'You forgot yourself for long enough to call me Lawson.'

CHAPTER EIGHT

ALONE once more, the door to her room firmly closed shut by Lawson, Ivory stood in exactly the same spot where Lawson had kissed her. Useless to try and get her chaotic thoughts into any kind of order. He expected her to go through into the sitting room to begin work any moment, and knowing she wouldn't welcome another visit from him—which would surely happen if she didn't show herself soon—she hurriedly changed into jeans and a loose-fitting top.

Still not believing that what had transpired had really happened, she ran her fingertips over her mouth, then shook her head as if trying to dismiss every remembered movement his lips had made against hers. Voices in the next room had her going over to the door to listen; she didn't think she could face Lawson again with a third person present—though wouldn't that be better than facing him alone? Her mind made up, she opened the door, but was just in time to see the door closing as someone went out.

Then her eyes avoiding Lawson who was standing with his back to the window, she saw that a trolley had been wheeled into the room and guessed that Lawson had ordered their meal to be sent up.

'I thought we could eat while I mapped out the format of the meeting I'm holding tomorrow,' he told her, coming away from the window. There was not the slightest intonation in his voice to give a hint that anything untoward had taken place.

At his complete lack of embarrassment, some of Ivory's

disquiet lessened, and she found herself able to look across at him. His dark eyes were regarding her with nothing but the same polite interest any employer would show his secretary.

Chagrined that he could completely put behind him the scene in her room, she determined he would know nothing from her manner of the way her mind was leapfrogging from one thought to another.

Lifting up the lid of one of the dishes, she exclaimed in what she hoped was her best unconcerned voice, 'Ah, steak and mushrooms—my favourite!'

Once they got down to work, it was business all the way, and much though she didn't want to, Ivory couldn't help but admire the neat turn of phrase Lawson had when dealing with all the points that had been put to him that afternoon.

Having got her notes sorted, there was quite a lot of typing for her to do, but as she moved to the typewriter Lawson told her she could leave most of it until the morning.

'If you could just type the notes I shall want to go over before I leave for the meeting,' he said. 'Then you can go to bed.'

'I don't mind typing the stuff that has to go back to London,' she told him—she was here to work after all even if it was now nearer ten than nine.

His, 'No,' was decisive. 'You look as though you should have been in bed hours ago.'

'Thanks,' she said shortly. She knew the effects of the sleepless night she had spent last night were catching up on her but there was no need for him to mention it. 'As a matter of fact I have not the slightest inclination to go to bed,' she added, more from bravado than anything, for she couldn't wait to get to her own room—she had a lot of thinking to do;

the work they had been doing had demanded her whole concentration. She was pulling out the chair in front of the table, when Lawson's voice reached her; she had been unaware he had been looking at her speculatively since her reply.

'You aren't—afraid to go to bed?' he asked suddenly.

'Afraid?' she questioned, not quite with him. Then as she realised he was referring for the first time to the way he had entered her bedroom and kissed her, the colour rose up in her face.

'Few ladies of my acquaintance blush prettily,' he said absently. Then returning to his question, 'You have nothing to fear, Ivory, I promise you.'

'I should think few ladies of your acquaintance blush, full stop,' she replied acidly before she could hold it back, and went red again. But instead of giving her a cold look as she'd expected, Lawson's face creased, and the sound of his all-male laughter came spilling out of him.

Fascinated that her sharpness had made him laugh, she stared at him. Unwanted flutterings started happening inside her, causing her to turn quickly away as she forced herself to concentrate on anything but the way his face lit up when he laughed—and the pleasure it gave her.

'You aren't worried, are you?' Lawson persisted, laughter gone from him now as he seemed ready to quieten every one of her fears.

'Good heavens,' she came back, her voice echoing in her ears, 'I'm not a child, you know—I have been kissed before.'

She didn't turn round to see what he made of that, but straightaway slammed all her energies into the typewriter. It didn't take long to complete the notes he wanted. Then, after looking through to check if she had made a mistake anywhere, she stood up and left the table.

Lawson was in one of the chairs writing furiously as ideas came into his head, making her loath to interrupt him. So she stood silently beside him looking down at his bent head, her heart hammering painfully. How could it have happened? she wondered, then ceased thinking when he looked up. Silently she handed him his notes.

'Thank you, Ivory.' His thoughts seemed still to be with the work in front of him. So she was unprepared for his, 'You're looking pale—are you all right?'

'I'm fine, thank you—though if there's nothing more you want me to do, I think I'll take your advice and go to bed.'

Not waiting for his answer, she left him, making herself walk steadily across the carpet and into her room. Once there she closed the door and leaned heavily against it, feeling momentarily as if her legs would hold her no longer.

'I'm in love with Lawson Alexander,' she breathed, as though by bringing it out into the open it would go away.

But it didn't go away. It stayed as she knew it would stay for evermore—the love she thought she had had for Michael paled into insignificance at the body blow fate had dealt her. She had no idea when it had started to happen—had thought at one time that she disliked him more than any other man she knew. Useless to try and dissect it and hope at the end that she could put it down to her imaginings, for all she tried—but to no avail.

Craftily, insidiously, this emotion had been waiting in the wings for just the right moment to pounce, she saw, as she came away from the door and prepared for bed. This then was at the root of the disturbed feelings she had had about him from almost the very beginning. The mercurial feelings she had had from the start—the dislike of him, the thoughts that he could be kind when he chose—oh, what was the point in trying to analyse it? Ivory got into her bed knowing she was in for another bad night.

But contrary to her expectations, she slept well. Maybe it was because she had been so tired, she reasoned on waking, maybe that was the reason she had dropped off after only ten minutes of watching the sliver of light that crept in from beneath the door. Or was it the subconscious feeling of security that Lawson was out there working and she was as close to him in person as she was ever likely to be?

Whatever the reason she felt rested, and since she was here to work, she'd better get up and get on with the typing she had left last night.

Lawson was already having his breakfast when she went in. The domesticity of seeing the man she loved eating breakfast hit her a body blow as the thought came of how she would like to do that every morning, but never would. Then Lawson was looking up from his paper and she forced a smile of greeting to her lips.

'There's coffee to spare,' Lawson said, indicating the pot. 'Help yourself. I wasn't sure what time you'd surface, so I didn't order your breakfast.'

That half an hour spent with him before he went out was something Ivory stored up to keep with her for ever. There had not been a cross word between them. It could have been, she realised afterwards, because she had been keeping a careful watch on her tongue, for he mustn't know by word or deed of her feelings for him. But whatever the cause, it had been delightful. She sat across the small table from him surreptitiously glancing his way every now and then, knowing he couldn't see her since he had again taken up his paper. He was wearing a light grey suit today; it fitted perfectly, she thought, and hurriedly dropped her eyes as he put his paper down.

'Aren't you ordering breakfast?' he enquired. 'Do you want me to . . .'

'No—no,' she said hastily. 'I normally only ever have a piece of toast.'

'There are a couple of pieces going begging there if you can't wait for them to bring fresh,' he offered. 'You'll have to use my plate, though.'

She savoured the moment of sharing his breakfast, of sharing his plate, and realised he must have ordered an extra cup and saucer since there were two of those. And that was thoughtful of him, she realised, and forgot herself so far as to mention the extra cup and saucer to him.

'I had thought to bring a cup of coffee in to you,' he said slowly, then paused, so she had a clear impression he was making the next bit up. 'But I wasn't sure you weren't a "tea" person first thing in the morning.'

She was sure as he said it that he was evading the truth, and whether because of the new feeling she had for him her senses were picking up things about him she had previously missed, she couldn't help but think he'd had every intention of bringing her coffee, but had thought at the last moment that she might be unnerved by waking up and finding him standing over her. He might even have thought she would think he had come to take up where his kiss had left off last night, she thought with sudden insight.

She glanced up and found his eyes on her. 'Thank you for the thought anyway,' she said, and smiled at him before looking away again. She was glad he hadn't come and wakened her, that was why she hadn't told him what her preference was first thing in the morning, tea or coffee. She knew if she awoke and found him there her eyes would be unguarded, her eyes would tell him much too much, she couldn't bear that her love should embarrass him.

Lawson stood up, and purely because she wanted him to

stay, she realised, she thought his voice sounded reluctant when he said, 'I must get going—wouldn't do to be late. These chaps are so touchy they'd be bound to see it as a slight.'

How long she would have sat there staring after him when he had gone she didn't know, but the waiter coming in to clear away the breakfast things brought her out of her reverie.

'Was breakfast to your liking, madam?' the waiter asked.

She was sure when the waiter had gone he must have thought she had overdone her assurances that the breakfast 'was perfect'. And knowing it wouldn't do to sit staring into space all morning, she settled down to work knowing Lawson wouldn't be very pleased if he came back finding she hadn't started.

Ivory felt happier with her discovery this morning than she had done last night. Oh, she knew that happiness couldn't last, but if everything between them until they returned to London could be as it had been this morning, it would be wonderful.

Lawson had gone out once more without giving her any indication of when he would be returning. So having finished her typing by one o'clock, she went down to lunch knowing she would be paged if a call came through from him. She was back in the suite by a quarter to two wondering what to do next. She didn't want to miss him when he returned, yet didn't want to sit in the hotel going over the same thoughts that plagued her at every idle moment. Common sense told her that since Lawson had not returned for lunch he was either going without or eating elsewhere. That being the case he must be working this afternoon, she reasoned, and schooled herself to stop dithering and get out into the fresh air.

On her way out she bumped into Michael, but he was in

too much of a hurry to do more than pass a few minutes with her. 'Sorry you couldn't make it last night, Ivory—I went out with some of my colleagues. We went to a night club, you'd have enjoyed it. You know, Go-Go dancers—that sort of thing.'

Ivory wasn't that sure she would have enjoyed it all that much, but said, 'It was a pity.'

'We have the sales dinner tonight—an all-male do,' he told her, 'otherwise I'd invite you—perhaps tomorrow night?'

'I'm not sure if I'll be free . . .'

'I'll give you a ring,' said Michael. 'Must dash—I have to address the boys this afternoon.'

How callow Michael now seemed, Ivory mused as she went through the front entrance of the hotel. And to think she had thought herself in love with him! Only now did she realise what a lucky escape they'd both had—they would have driven each other up the wall inside a year.

She was back in the hotel for five and went straight up to the suite. She would love a cup of tea, but first just had to check whether Lawson had come back.

He had. And any idea that they might continue in the same easy atmosphere they had shared at breakfast was rudely knocked on the head.

'Where the hell have you been?' he snapped at her, barely waiting for her to close the door behind her.

'Did you want me for something?' she asked innocently, thinking something must have gone badly wrong with his meeting.

'Since you're here as my secretary, I would have thought it not expecting too much to hope to find you here when I got back.'

She wouldn't lose her temper, she wouldn't. If he'd had a

sticky time this morning, she knew it would be she who would end up getting the worst of any argument between them.

'You didn't say what time you'd be back,' she said, in what she thought was a reasonable tone. 'I thought since you stayed out to lunch, you must intend working all afternoon.'

'You didn't think to leave word at the desk to say where you'd gone?'

It hadn't occurred to her to do so. 'No,' she said shortly knowing her control was in danger of slipping, 'I didn't think of it.'

'Perhaps in future you *would* think of it,' he said icily. 'Where have you been anyway?'

'I went out for a walk.'

'On your own?'

'Of course on my own.'

'You haven't seen the boy-friend?'

'Boy-friend?' she echoed. 'You mean Michael?'

'How many boy-friends do you have staying in this hotel?'

'You're mad because you think I'm spending the time the company is paying me to in . . .'

'That's got nothing to do with it,' Lawson broke in coldly. 'I've told you before, while you're away with me you are under my protection—I don't intend taking you back to London suffering the consequences of unrequited love a second time around.'

'How dare you!' she flared, the frail threads of her temper snapping at last. 'Who do you think you are to interfere in my life? If I want to run the risk of having the door slammed in my face a second time I'll do it. But since you're so concerned you might cast your mind back to last evening.' Her eyes were flashing in a veritable inferno of anger— either that or go under and submit weakly every time he

chose to think he could say what he liked to her. 'I take it
that kiss I was forced to suffer was part of your therapy for
getting Michael out of my system—you may remember I
told you he had no power to affect me at all.'

With that she charged past him, only just holding back
the tears. She made it to her room and banged the door
tight shut, and was shaking so badly she had to sit down.
What had got into him she couldn't think, but she just
wasn't going to take everything he hurled at her lying down.
What would it have mattered if she *had* spent the afternoon
with Michael? She was positive Lawson hadn't wanted her
for anything—his meeting had gone badly awry, she
guessed, and he'd had to take it out on somebody, and because she hadn't been here when he'd got back he'd picked
on any excuse to use her as his whipping boy.

It took some minutes, but after a while she got herself
under control. She knew she would have to go out into the
other room some time, though didn't want to; she would far
rather be a million miles away. She tried to think of
anything—anything other than what had happened since
she had so innocently come along the corridor and entered
the sitting room. She recalled that she'd had nothing more
serious on her mind then than the need for a cup of tea. Why
should she deprive herself of a cup of tea just because he was
in a foul mood? she wondered, and without more ado she
picked up the phone and asked for tea to be sent up.

'Is it for one or two?' the enquiry came back, which had
her stopping to think for a moment.

And when in all fairness she couldn't drink tea without
offering him a cup—she didn't want to remember he had
shared his coffee with her only that morning—she asked for
tea for two, declining the offer of cakes.

Going over to the door she listened hard. There were no

sounds of Lawson moving about—and only when she heard a knock on the outer door did she open her bedroom door and go through.

'I'll get it,' she said, seeing Lawson sitting with his mind deeply absorbed in some papers. She told the waiter where to put the tray, waited until he'd closed the door when he departed, then offered, 'Tea?' and was glad to hear her voice sounded normal.

Lawson left what he was doing and came over to where she was standing, holding out his hand for his cup and saucer. 'Still mad with me?' he enquired, his own tones even.

Still mad with him? She'd thought he had been equally angry with her when she'd stormed to her room. Unable to find her voice, unspeaking she handed him his tea, and felt the pull of his eyes compelling her to look up. She fought the compulsion to look at him, and when she still hadn't answered, heard him ask quietly:

'Truce, Ivory?'

The softly spoken words had the effect she thought he must have been after, for her head came up and her eyes flicked him a hasty glance before she looked away again. 'Truce,' she agreed.

She found Lawson was too much of a man to hold a grudge, and trying to be as big, buried the remains of her anger when he began telling her how his day had gone. From what he was saying, she could only gather that his meeting had gone very well indeed, which put her further into confusion as to why he had been so very angry when she had come in. Perhaps he had been telling the truth after all, she mused, and did look on himself as her protector when they were working away from the office.

'So it looks as though the dispute will soon be over?' she asked him.

'All being well.'

'And we'll be going home soon?' Now that her anger had passed, she was disappointed that her time with him in Manchester was at an end, but didn't dare let her disappointment show in her face.

'You want to go back?'

There was that sharpness back in his voice again. 'I'm not bothered,' she told him, mustering calm.

Lawson gave her a searching look as though suspecting she had other motives for staying, and Ivory gave a sigh—she just couldn't win. But when Lawson spoke again his voice was back to normal—whether he'd heard her sigh or not she didn't know.

'We'd better hang on here a couple more days just in case something blows up,' he told her. Then, their tea finished, he told her he had some notes he would like her to take down, adding, 'You haven't made any arrangements for dinner tonight, have you?'

'No, not tonight,' she replied, knowing if she had he would straightway tell her to cancel them—though they were coming along since he had bothered to ask at all, she supposed.

He was too astute not to notice from her reply that she wasn't answering for any other night. 'You mean you have something fixed up for tomorrow?'

Whether he thought she was heading for another dose of heartbreak with Michael or not, she found herself forced into telling him, 'I bumped into Michael today. He has a sales dinner on tonight—he said he'd give me a call tomorrow.'

She waited for the acid to come pouring out of Lawson, but when none came she looked at him, and saw he was studying her closely. 'I see,' was all he said, then he got down to the business of giving her dictation.

Any hopes she might have nurtured of sharing coffee with him the next morning, of again recapturing that brief half an hour yesterday when not one single cross word had taken place, were doomed as soon as she opened her bedroom door. A fully dressed Lawson greeted her, briefcase in hand, obviously on his way out, and in no mood for idle chit-chat.

He barely paused when he saw her in the doorway, saying tersely, 'I spoke too soon when I said the dispute was almost over. I've just had a call to say pickets are out on the gates stopping my workers from going in.'

'You're going to the works?' She tried to say it coolly, but it came out in a rush as a vivid picture flashed through her mind of the man she loved having a half brick hurled at his head by some lout who didn't know any better.

'Worried about me?' It was the first time she'd seen that look on his face, part serious, part mocking, and she knew he had sensed her fear.

'Who'll drive me home if you get laid out unconscious?'

She wished he wouldn't grin like that, it made her legs go all wobbly.

'I shall have to take care to duck, shan't I?'

She paced agitatedly round the sitting room after he had gone trying to blot out indescribable pictures of him being hurt or maimed for life. She'd love him whatever state he was in—but she knew that to be wheelchair-bound for the rest of his life was something he would never console himself to. She was being absurd she told herself. Lawson was tough—he could take care of himself. She spotted his bedroom door open and went forward to close it, then left it as it was—it seemed more as if he was still with her that way, as though at any moment he would come through that door and start bossing her about. As long as he came back safely, she thought she wouldn't mind how bossy he was with her.

She spent most of the morning typing out Lawson's notes, though she had to confess her mind wasn't really on her work. Several times she had to get up and walk around, as if by the very act of movement she would return to her typewriter with her mind cleared.

After lunch she again went out. To stay in the hotel and await Lawson's return just wasn't on; she was too unsettled to sit hour after hour just watching the door for his return. Yesterday he had returned only just before her, she remembered. It had been about five then. At four she returned to the hotel—she wouldn't order tea until he came in. He would tell her about his day and even if he made her cross by one of his sharp remarks, she wouldn't rise to it, she promised herself.

The apartment was empty when she went in—well, she hadn't expected him back. She glanced at his door; it was still open the way she had instructed the chambermaid to leave it. Perhaps she'd better go and close it. But before she could start across the carpet, a knock sounded on the outside door and she opened it to find Michael standing there.

'Oh, hello,' she said, clearing her mind rapidly to wonder what Michael's visit was in aid of, then feeling her 'Hello' had sounded a bit offhand, added, 'I've only just come in.'

'I've just come in myself,' Michael told her. 'I thought as I was going to my room I'd come and see you rather than telephone.'

Aware that she was not being very gracious keeping him standing at the door, though she didn't want him still here when Lawson came back, Ivory invited him in. Lawson thought she had no pride where Michael was concerned for all she'd told him Michael meant nothing to her now—but she didn't want to risk his displeasure by finding Michael here when he returned.

'How's your conference going?' she asked, just to be polite. But her good manners, she found, were wasted, as Michael stared round the apartment.

'Ye gods, you've done well for yourself!' he exclaimed. 'They've put me in what must be the smallest room in the hotel, and here you are—a secretary with a whole suite to lounge about in!'

'I—er—' She felt the red colour of embarrassment come up under her skin, and knew she would have to let him think she had the whole apartment to herself—she just couldn't explain, she realised; this new Michael would never understand—she doubted that the old one would have done either. But she reckoned without him seeing the tell-tale colour in her cheeks.

'Where does your boss sleep?' he asked shrewdly, and she'd never noticed that cunning look in his eyes before.

'Actually,' she answered, knowing there was nothing for it but to tell him, 'this is a two-bedroomed suite—I messed up the booking . . .'

'And which bedroom do you both use?' Michael said nastily. Lost for words, Ivory just stared open-mouthed at him. 'My God, you've changed! What happened to the frigid virgin? You never let me take you to bed, and you were supposed to be in love with me.' Ivory closed her mouth as nausea hit her. 'Or have you never changed—were you always anybody's, just putting on an act with me because you thought you'd found somebody fool enough to want to marry you, not wanting me to know until it was too late that I was just one of a long line . . .'

'Get out!' Ivory found her voice.

'I'm going, don't fret.' She saw he was looking ugly now —he hadn't been very prepossessing before. 'But before I go I'll have what should have been mine a long time ago.'

A lustful look came over his face causing a small scream

of pure fright to escape her as the horrifying thought came of—Oh, my God, he's going to rape me!

Then as Michael made a grab for her a cool voice behind her said, 'You'd better stop right there,' and while her mind was still registering the fact that miraculously Lawson was back and was ordering Michael out, she whirled round and saw him standing there in his shirt sleeves, and realised with a feeling of utter degradation that he must have been in his bedroom listening all the time.

She looked at Michael, saw the incredulous look on his face that would have been comical had she not felt like screaming, screaming, screaming, and dragged her eyes back to Lawson and saw in his eyes a look of pure, granite hard intent as he advanced towards Michael.

Unable to take any more, she wheeled quickly round and only just made it to her room before heartrending sobs shook her—she was oblivious to the sounds behind her, was completely unaware that Michael had been hurled bodily into the corridor, the door slammed shut behind him.

She felt defiled, disgusted, and most of all ashamed that Lawson had heard all those terrible things Michael had said about her. And those words, together with the fact that if Lawson had not been there Michael would have . . .

Fresh sobs broke from her. She hadn't heard Lawson come into her room, and as his hand lightly touched her shoulder she jerked away, her tear-flooded eyes just making out it was Lawson who had followed her and not Michael. Then as she made another involuntary movement, this time towards him, she felt Lawson's arms go round her and the comforting wall of his chest beneath her face, and sobbed against him as though her heart would break.

'That's enough now,' she heard his voice, gentle but firm above her head. 'You've had one hell of a fright, but it's all over now.'

He still held her, his hands splayed out against her back, and she was glad about that—it didn't seem wrong that he should be the one to comfort her. But as her sobs gradually lessened and her tears became only an occasional trickle, she realised he must be hating like mad having found himself in this situation.

'It . . . It wasn't t-true, what he s-said—about me being any . . . anybody's,' she said, pushing herself away from him, only to find herself pulled back against him as her voice wobbled on the last word.

'I know.'

Just those two little words, but they were said with such conviction—not placatorily as if he'd agree with anything if it would stop her crying, but 'I know' as if as far as he was concerned there was no doubt about it. Those two small words did more to stem her tears than anything else he could have said.

'I'm sorry for what he said about y-you and me,' she said, glad to find some of her composure returning at last.

'I think I can bear it.'

Ivory lifted her head to look at him with tear-stormed eyes. Lawson was looking at her kindly, seeming not at all embarrassed at the position he found himself in, and it was Ivory who flushed and turned her face away.

'I'm glad you came in when you did,' she said, and shuddered in horror at what might have happened. She felt Lawson's arms tighten around her and thought he guessed what she was thinking.

'Try to forget about it—nothing happened.'

She heard a hard note enter his voice and knew Lawson would have beaten Michael to a pulp if he had succeeded in his intention—After all, she was here under his protection wasn't she?

'I didn't know you were back.' Involuntarily she clutched

at his waist, and felt his warmth through the silky feel of his shirt.

'I hadn't been in long,' Lawson told her, seeming to know she had to talk it all out of her system. 'I was in the act of changing when I heard you at the door. I wasn't expecting you for another hour or so—but I thought better than to present myself in my underpants when I heard you come in.'

There was a teasing note in his voice now, and she knew he was trying to get her to smile. She lifted her head to look at him, and had to smile, for all it was only a very weak effort.

'You heard everything?' she asked, hoping he hadn't—though not wanting to recall any of it if that was the case and he wanted her to tell him what had been said.

'Yes, I heard,' he said grimly, the teasing note gone.

'I had no idea Michael was like that,' she said half to herself. 'None of that showed through when I was engaged to him.'

'Never?'

She shook her head. 'No, never once, though . . .' She stopped, embarrassed once more.

'Though?' Lawson prompted.

'Well, I . . . er . . . told you Michael threw me over. I suppose the reason he gave me should have given me some indication.'

She wished she hadn't said that, but then she relaxed, for it seemed she wasn't going to have to explain, for Lawson had pieced everything together quite ably by himself.

'He threw you over because you insisted on wedding bells before bed?'

'Yes,' she whispered, then couldn't look him in the eyes any more, and turned her head to stare at his open-necked shirt front. He still held her in his arms, loose though his hold was, and she was dreading the moment when he took his arms away, because for all of the trauma that had gone on a short while ago, she was happy in his arms. She realised Lawson was waiting for her to add more, realised he wasn't satisfied with the simple 'Yes' she had given him. 'He said if I loved him I wouldn't hesitate,' she said huskily.

'Then the man must be as insensitive as hell. Anyone with half an eye can see there's a quality in you that needs gentle handling to bring out the fire, not sledgehammer tactics,' Lawson said in a cold voice.

CHAPTER NINE

LAWSON had just said there was a quality in her that needed gentle handling—he had also said anyone with half an eye could see it, but Ivory didn't think about that then; she was only concerned with his perception.

'Is there?' she questioned softly. 'I don't know . . .' she began, then continued, her voice growing stronger, 'I don't know about that. I've always been a bit—reserved—that way.'

'I suspected as much,' said Lawson, and this time his voice was very gentle. 'Don't worry about what he told you —it will come right for you when you meet the right man.'

Since she was now looking at the one man she considered to be the right man, Ivory felt she couldn't in all honesty answer anything to that. And then, as though suspecting she was still in need of some sort of comfort, Lawson bent his head and laid his lips on hers and kissed her.

Unafraid, Ivory still had her hands clasped loosely at his waist, and she didn't move. Then Lawson lifted his mouth away from hers and looked at her. She thought she saw a teasing look return to his face and said softly and truthfully:

'That was nice.'

'I'll agree,' Lawson replied. 'But it could prove to be dangerous medicine.'

'That's what it was, wasn't it? Something to make me feel better.' She hadn't meant her voice to sound challenging—it just came out that way.

The humour disappeared from his face, but she was still

unafraid, as she looked back at him. 'Obviously the dosage wasn't strong enough,' he said, his tones cool. Then once more his lips were on hers, and this time, although still undemanding, there was something about his kiss, and she knew he was no longer out to comfort her. Though his lips were gentle as they rested against hers, she knew if she wanted to come out of this in one piece she had better take the necessary action and pull away from him—that was all that was needed—she knew he would let her go without argument.

But she didn't pull away, and the very gentle way he held her, his lips only lightly touching hers, made her want more, made her want him to kiss her as if he really meant it.

Involuntarily her hands tightened on his waist, and although he did not take his mouth away from hers Lawson stilled in his movement, as though thinking her movement was to indicate that she was afraid. Of their own accord her lips parted beneath his, and at her acceptance, the pressure of his mouth over hers increased and she felt him pulling her closer to him.

Unable to resist the pleasure his lips offered, she pressed to get nearer to him, while warning bells inside her head went off ignored. As one, they moved slightly, and it was no surprise to her when she felt the bed come up against her legs. When she felt Lawson gently take her down on to the bed with him, she was still unafraid—glad if anything that because of their unequal height by lying down she could get closer to him.

She thought she whispered his name, but she wasn't sure. Then his mouth was scorching a path across her throat, his fingers unerringly unbuttoning the top three buttons of her blouse, and she felt his mouth doing crazy things across the swell of her breasts. She faltered only when his hand came to cup her breast, his fingers in the same movement pulling her blouse further open to reveal the throbbing swell of her to his gaze. She wanted to undo the buttons of his shirt in turn, wanted to run her hands over his naked chest, but after she had raised one hand tentatively towards his shirt, he looked at her and her hand dropped away as she saw the smouldering desire in his eyes.

'I wish I knew what to do to please you—I wish I knew more,' she whispered, her voice choking in her throat, her colour high that the look he was sending her way was for her alone.

She wished for quite some time afterwards that she hadn't spoken. For if Lawson had shaken his head to clear it, she couldn't have been more certain her words had stopped him in his tracks. She saw his teeth clamp hard together, heard the pull of his sharply indrawn breath—as though he was fighting for control—then heard him say on a ragged note:

'Thank God for your innocence, Ivory—it only just saved you.' He then got up quickly, and without so much as looking at her again, he left the room.

Ivory rolled over on the bed and buried her head in its tumbled covers. She was useless—useless. She hadn't been able to give herself to the man she thought she loved—and when she'd wanted to give herself to the man she *did* love, he had refused to take what she was offering.

She should be feeling ashamed, she knew, that she had so blatantly wanted Lawson to make love to her, but she wasn't. She loved him—it seemed so right. All her careful upbringing had fallen away when she had been in his arms. Oh God, she wanted him!

Slowly sanity began to return, and with it the embarrassment she had not felt earlier. What had she done? Lawson had intimated she would come alive with gentle handling, and he had been right. Though she was sure that hadn't been his intention when he had gently begun to kiss her. After that she'd shown him clearly that she wanted him. It was no good at all arguing that he in turn wanted her—men were different. She knew he wasn't in love with her and knew she just wouldn't be able to face him again now that he must know she was in love with him. But she felt powerless to get off the bed—with everything within her screaming for her to run away and hide she knew she had to stay exactly where she was until she heard the outer door click, heard him go out. Only then would she dare leave her room.

'Sit up, Ivory.'

She hadn't heard him come into her room. She stayed where she was—she just couldn't look him in the eyes.

'I said sit up!'

There was an authoritative note in his voice that had to be answered. She rolled herself round into a sitting position, but still couldn't look at him.

'Button your blouse,' he commanded, and her face flamed scarlet when she looked down and saw that most of her breasts covered in a lacy bra were open to his view. Going at it too quickly, her trembling fingers fumbled over the buttons. Her skirt had ridden up and she pushed it down over her knees, though she considered it a bit late in the day to discover her modesty.

Thinking she could never look into his face again, she heard the words, 'Oh hell!' break from him, and her eyes flew to his face. She saw his hair was clinging darkly to his head and presumed he had showered. Guardedly she looked at him, watched while he went and sat in a chair away from her, and she felt she wanted to die as the thought hit her that men lost all interest in women who threw themselves at them.

Lawson didn't stay seated for very long. He seemed restless, and she thought it was more from distaste of the situation than from anything else that he got up from his chair. He didn't come any nearer to her and he looked as if he was making his mind up about something. Then the bombshell fell.

'Get packed—we're going back to London.'

That effectively loosened her tongue. 'Back to London?' she echoed, startled. Lawson didn't waste time arguing.

'Get packed,' he snapped, and left her to get on with it.

They had been driving for an hour before Lawson said anything. He had asked her before they left if she wanted dinner, and she'd given him a short, 'No.' She felt if she tried to push anything down she'd be violently ill. He hadn't eaten either, though there were a couple of packets of sandwiches resting on the back seat. He'd obviously asked the catering staff at the hotel for them lest they were hungry on the way back, but they lay where he had tossed them, forgotten.

When Lawson had driven for an hour without saying anything, she wondered if he had the works on his mind. She didn't flatter herself she had any place in his thoughts. He must have completed the job he'd gone to Manchester to do, probably would have discussed it with her before telling her they were returning to London—only he hadn't had time, for no sooner had he got in than she had arrived and after her Michael. She tried to strangle the groan that rose to her throat, but part of it escaped, and Lawson heard it.

'I came to your room to talk to you,' he said, tight-lipped.

'Which time?' Only by being flippant could she hope to get out of this with any rags of pride left.

'Both times,' he said shortly. 'It seems today has been your day for traumatic experiences, Ivory—and I hold myself partly to blame.'

'You?' she said, startled, and about to ask why he considered himself to blame, stopped short, realising that the least she said the better if she didn't want to condemn herself utterly in his eyes.

'Yes, me,' Lawson confirmed. 'When that apology for manhood left, I came in hoping to help you over the experience. I knew you were upset—I should never have kissed you.'

'I . . . I . . .' Ivory felt she ought to say something, but her mind seemed to be caught in a vacuum. Then Lawson was continuing and she was glad it was dark in the car, for the last thing she wanted him to witness was the growing amazement in her face as he went on.

'You were still in a state of shock—you hadn't recovered from the fright he gave you. I should have seen you were in no way capable of coping with another emotional upset—I was completely in the wrong to kiss you.'

'You only did it to comfort me,' she felt impelled to put in. For if she had been having a hard time ever since he'd got up from the bed, it was clear now that Lawson was positively hating all of his part in it.

Some of the tightness went out of him at her understanding of his initial intention. 'I shouldn't have let it go any further,' he said. Then he was telling her he had come back into her room to have this talk with her, then shatteringly, he was apologising, saying, 'Will you forgive me for the fright I gave you?'

Ivory was quiet for some minutes. He must know she had been his for the taking. He must know. Yet here he was taking all the blame on himself—excusing the way she had responded to him by saying she was still in emotional shock before he had begun kissing her. She came alive to the realisation that if Lawson believed all that, then she was safe—he couldn't have discovered how much she loved him.

'Well, will you forgive me?' he was asking, when she hadn't answered.

'Of course,' Ivory found her voice. 'I . . . I'd like to forget all about it . . . if we could.'

Lawson didn't answer her. In fact he barely spoke again until he was drawing up outside her door. 'Don't come to the office tomorrow,' he told her.

Having spent a restless night haunted by the fact that she had so nearly given herself away, Ivory got out of bed the next morning with every intention of going to work. But as she seated herself before her dressing table mirror and stared back at the washed-out face, the eyes that still showed evidence of her bout of weeping—for she had been unable to stem the flow of tears when telling Mandy some of what had happened—she knew she just couldn't go to the office that day. She would be on pins all day until she saw Lawson again; she flunked completely at the idea of coming up against him face to face.

Knowing she was being cowardly, she stayed at home and busied herself tidying up the flat. Mandy had been very sympathetic, she recalled. If she'd been more bracing perhaps she would have managed to hold the tears back, she thought now. But Mandy's eyes had grown wide and nearly popped out of her head when Ivory had told her how vile Michael had been. 'You really think he would have . . .' Mandy had been unable to go on. 'Thank God Lawson Alexander was there!' And as Mandy said those words, Ivory had been unable to check a sob. Mandy had grown thoughtful for a moment, then said quietly, 'You're in love with this Lawson Alexander man, aren't you?'

She was glad it wasn't so obvious to him, and she knew if she wanted to keep her secret away from him, the only road left open to her was to hand in her resignation. She spent most of that day being torn this way and that. How could she give up a job she enjoyed so much—she'd been stimulated by the work she was doing more than any other job she had ever done. That she'd only had three jobs since she'd left secretarial college was neither here nor there. And if she was to be totally honest—now that she knew herself in love with Lawson, would that stimulation be there if she was doing the same work but for another man? She doubted it.

Mrs Stavely seemed surprised to see her when she arrived at the office shortly before nine the following day. 'I thought you were still in Manchester?' she greeted her.

Hadn't Lawson been into the office himself yesterday? He couldn't have, she realised instantly, otherwise why Mrs Stavely's surprise! 'Er—I wasn't well,' she told the senior secretary, stretching a point. 'Mr Alexander brought me home on Wednesday night.'

'Ah, that explains it,' said Mrs Stavely, who didn't like loose ends. 'I expect Mr Alexander returned to Manchester to clear up this business.'

Ivory sat at her desk feeling worse than ever. She still hadn't decided what to do about leaving, but since Lawson had returned to Manchester, presumably without a secretary, it looked as if he could manage quite well without her. She was glad, though, that he was still away; today was Friday—if she didn't see him again until Monday, that would give her the whole weekend to make up her mind what she was going to do about leaving. At the moment she couldn't face the thought of never seeing him again.

Later that morning she was in Mrs Stavely's office when the phone rang. She heard Mrs Stavely speak sharply to someone at the other end, and presumed from the conversation that someone in the buying department was going to get a rocket, for Mrs Stavely rarely spoke sharply to anyone. 'I'll come down and look into it myself,' she heard her say, and was just returning the file she had borrowed when she heard Mrs Stavely say, 'Would you mind keeping an ear open for the phone, Ivory—I shouldn't be more than ten minutes.'

It amused her to see Mrs Stavely march out of the office like a warship of old in full sail—she wouldn't like to be in the buying department when she arrived there. Her thoughts were cut short when the telephone rang, and she went across to answer it.

'Mr Alexander's office,' she said, as she'd heard Mrs Stavely say many times before.

'Can I speak with Mr Alexander?' said a faintly accented, familiar voice, then hesitation as the voice asked, 'Is that you, Ivory?'

'Jan!' she exclaimed. 'Yes, it is me—Lawson isn't here today—can I take a message for you? I don't think he'll be here until Monday.'

'No matter . . .' She lost what else Jan was saying because the door leading into Lawson's office opened and Lawson stood there, tall, dark-suited, and with a dark unfathomable look on his face as he looked back at her. Unnerved because she hadn't known he was in his office, hadn't heard him enter his room by way of the corridor, Ivory turned her back on him and tried to catch up with what Jan was saying.

'I'm sorry, Jan, I missed that bit . . .'

'I said I was hoping to ring you early this evening—but from London.'

'Oh, you're coming over?' She tried to sound pleased, had forgotten the disquiet she had felt over Jan's visit, but was overwhelmingly conscious that Lawson was still standing behind her. And when Jan asked her if she would have dinner with him that night, her only thought was that not by word or deed should Lawson find out how she felt about him.

'I'd like that very much,' she said more warmly than she would otherwise have done. 'What time shall I be ready?'

It was only as she put the phone down, her mind registering that Jan would be calling for her at eight that night, that she remembered Jan had asked to speak to Lawson when she'd answered his call. Controlling her features, she turned to face him.

'Jan really rang to speak with you,' she told him.

'It damn well sounded like it!' was her answer before the door slammed shut in her face.

She was glad he annoyed her. At least being angry with him stopped her moping over him. She'd forgotten what an arrogant beast he was, and as the day wore on and she encountered him once in Mrs Stavely's office and once when Mrs Stavely asked her to take some papers into him, she thought that anyone coming in from outside would think they were sworn enemies, the way he was short with her and the way it took her all her time to be civil back to him in return.

Happily five o'clock came at last, but Lawson was in Mrs Stavely's office when Ivory popped her head round the door to say goodnight to her. 'Goodnight, Mrs Stavely,' she said, then realising it would look odd if she left him out, added, 'Goodnight, Mr Alexander.'

She should have saved her breath, she fumed, as she followed the other clicking heels down the stairs—there was always a queue for the lifts at this time of night—for he hadn't answered her. Oh, she was definitely giving in her notice, she thought, her anger against him growing. She couldn't work for a man who was on the one hand ready to take the blame for everything that had happened, but then on the other snapping at her at every turn. She was sure now he had no idea of her feelings—had he known, she reasoned having seen a gentler side to his nature, he would not have snapped at her but would have treated her with an unbearable kindness. There had been no sign of an unbearable kindness today; if anything, she saw, a sudden light breaking through, he was no different today than he had ever been with her—it was only her own sense of awareness that magnified every little incident.

Dinner with Jan was not a great success. She was still too raw from her encounters with Lawson that day to be able to relax. Fortunately, Jan didn't seem to notice anything out of the way, but when he took her home, partly because she was feeling mean for having her thoughts for most of the evening with another man, and partly because it was still quite early, Ivory invited him in.

'Your friend Mandy is not in tonight,' Jan observed when she handed him a cup of coffee and joined him on the settee.

'No, she's gone to a party and won't be back until late,' Ivory explained, and then because for all he was a well-to-do diamond merchant, Jan was sometimes a little old-fashioned, 'You don't mind that we're on our own?'

Jan gave her a warm look that told her he wasn't that old-fashioned, then said, 'Not at all. In fact I am rather pleased we shall be on our own. I wanted to talk to you this weekend—I think now is perhaps the right moment.'

But it wasn't. She should have seen it coming; had done, she owned after he had gone, only like an ostrich she'd buried her head in the sand. And now Jan had gone away saying he could see no point in staying in London any longer; he had hoped when he had left Holland that when he asked her to marry him, she would agree.

'I'm sorry Jan,' she'd said regretfully, and because he was such a nice person and she felt dreadful that she'd hurt him so, 'I'm truly sorry,' she whispered, and not wanting him any more upset than he already was, managed to hold back the tears that had been choking her until he had gone.

Once the door had closed behind him, she let go with a vengeance until at last her tears dried and she went into the kitchen to make herself another coffee. She couldn't hold back the thought that she'd had enough emotion this week to last her a lifetime. In barely a week, she had changed from a girl who stayed in at nights—except when Jan came over, she amended, as she blew her nose for what she hoped would be the last time—to a girl who had gone through the emotional battering of first Michael, then Lawson, and now Jan.

Picking up her coffee, she nearly made it into the sitting room, when the phone rang, halting her in her stride. Looking at the clock she saw it was ten past twelve. Who on earth would be ringing at this time of night? It didn't take her long to find out—and had she known it was Lawson, in no more pleasant a humour than he had been the last time she had seen him, she wouldn't have answered the phone at all. She was already far from being her normal self—she didn't need any of his stringent comments to add to her collection of dejected feelings.

'What do you want?' she asked, her voice anything but gracious.

'Am I interrupting something?'

'Ten past midnight is hardly the most convenient time to call,' she snapped, meaning just that. But Lawson chose to put his own interpretation on why it might be inconvenient, and it infuriated her.

'I take it Jan is still with you, and I am interrupting

something. Am I to believe I triggered off a latent streak of permissiveness in you?'

At any other time she would have thought he was making one of his teasing jibes. But she had been emotionally upset before his call, and was in no mood to appreciate his sense of humour. Maybe it was because she was upset already, but his meaning was painfully clear, and she saw red.

'Some men—' she began, and tried a deep breath to calm herself, but it didn't work. 'Some men,' she repeated, 'are more interested in a more permanent relationship than a passing affair.'

She knew she shouldn't have said that—the tense pause at the other end told her that before her own common sense asserted itself. What she'd had with Lawson could in no way be called an affair, for all she knew that at that moment in Manchester he had briefly desired her.

'Am I to take it Jan has proposed to you?' Lawson asked, his voice completely detached, as if it wasn't the slightest interest to him.

Anger, mainly against herself for wanting Lawson to be devastated that she could contemplate marrying Jan, had her snapping, 'If you must know—he did!'

Complete silence reigned the other end, then, 'And are you going to marry him?'

'Mind your own business!' Ivory stormed down the phone, before slamming it back on its cradle.

She wouldn't cry again—she wouldn't, she vowed as she walked away from the phone. It was a mystery to her how she could love Lawson so much yet hate him so much at the same time.

Eventually she calmed down sufficiently to realise her overstrung emotions were looking for slights from Lawson where there were probably none intended. Like playing back a tape, she went over her telephone conversation with him, and realised that the inflection in his tone when he spoke of 'triggering off a latent streak of permissiveness' had been his way of saying he believed the very opposite of her.

Oh God, she wished she could go to sleep and wake up and find her month's notice at Alexander's had been worked out and that she was working somewhere where she might never run the risk of seeing him again—wake up and find herself completely cured of this emotion that was rocking her very foundations.

The weekend passed, and by the time Monday came around Ivory was feeling more able to cope. She wasn't looking forward to her interview with Lawson at all. How could she have lost control so completely as to tell him to mind his own business, and then to slam the phone down on him?

Over the last couple of days she had had time to see Lawson's purpose in ringing her flat on Friday night had been in order to speak with Jan—Jan had telephoned the office to speak with him on Friday and it could have been that they were negotiating some business deal which had come to a head and necessitated Lawson wanting to contact him. She had puzzled the point that midnight was a bit late to be conducting business—but who knew what went on in the gigantic deals of big business.

Mrs Stavely was already in the office when Ivory arrived, making her realise that the promise she had made to herself that one of these days she would make a special effort and be the first to arrive might never come to fruition since she had decided to give in her notice today, that gave her one month in which to achieve her ambition.

'Have a nice weekend?' Mrs Stavely greeted her.

'Lovely, thank you,' Ivory answered, trying to put some

enthusiasm into the lie. 'How did your weekend go?'

'Quite nice, actually—Jenny has been asking Leonard and me to go and have a look at her new baby, and since it was so nice yesterday we went over to see her.'

'How is Jenny?' Ivory asked, and they talked for some minutes about Jenny and her young son who had been named Jonathan after his father John. Then Mrs Stavely said something that had Ivory giving her double attention.

'Jonathan is such a gorgeous little chap I don't know how Jenny will be able to leave him when the time comes.'

'Leave him?'

'Well, yes—you knew she was coming back to her old job after the baby's birth, didn't you?'

'I . . . No, I didn't,' Ivory said honestly, and wondered if she had gone as pale as she felt. It was one thing to have decided the only thing to do was to hand in her resignation —but quite another to learn she would be redundant anyway.

'You mean Mr Alexander didn't tell you you were only to be here temporarily?'

'No,' Ivory said quietly, feeling suddenly weak at the knees.

'This is really too bad!' exclaimed Mrs Stavely, showing signs of something other than her unflappable self for the first time since Ivory had known her. 'You should have been told in writing that you were only here temporarily—I specifically asked Mr Alexander about it because we have to be so careful not to contravene the Employment Protection Act.' Mrs Stavely then went on to explain—although Ivory only vaguely heard her—that an expectant mother who had been employed by the same firm for so long had the right under the Act to return to her job within a certain time after her confinement. 'Mr Alexander doesn't much care for the idea of mothers leaving their children in other people's care I know,' Mrs Stavely went on, 'though understanding about the high mortgage repayments some of his staff have, and he plans to find space for a crêche to be provided.'

All this was very well, Ivory thought, and very illustrious of him, she felt sure. But she couldn't help the feeling of hurt that he had left her to find out he had never intended to keep her on permanently. That she had no intention of staying had nothing to do with it.

Mrs Stavely seemed to realise all this talk about plans for a crêche were in no way going to help Ivory, and a regretful look came over her face as she came back to the point. 'I'm terribly sorry, my dear—this must have been something of a shock for you, and I've so enjoyed having you working with me.'

This was high praise indeed, and at any other time Ivory would have been thrilled to think she had passed muster with Mrs Stavely. But just then all she could think was— why hadn't Lawson told her? Did she count for so little that he didn't think it worthwhile mentioning that Jenny would be coming back?

'Is Mr Alexander fully booked up today?' she asked. 'I'd like to see him if he's not too busy.'

Mrs Stavely noted the mutinous expression on Ivory's face, and smiled regretfully. 'He won't be in today,' she said gently.

'Oh!' Ivory felt deflated. She had been ready for him. By tomorrow she might have cooled down, though at the moment she felt she'd be on the boil for a week.

'I rang him at home on Saturday morning about a firm whose name I couldn't remember when he asked me on Friday—we hadn't dealt with them for years and it came to me as I'd got my hands in the washing up bowl. He was just leaving for the airport when I rang—some business or other in Oslo. He should be in tomorrow—anything I can help you with?'

Ivory went back to her desk after declining Mrs Stavely's offer. She would know it was something to do with the news she had given her about Jenny.

She was glad to be busy that morning, for it gave her little time to think, and thinking she found was a useless exercise since all her thoughts went round and round like the swings at a fair ground, and with about the same result, for by the time it came for her to go to lunch, she was so churned up with the thoughts that had seeped through, she was feeling physically sick.

It couldn't go on, the see-sawing backwards and forwards, and after avoiding the mêlée in the canteen, deciding she wouldn't be able to eat anyway, Ivory walked for almost an hour and came back to the office, selected a sheet of plain paper and typed her resignation. That she made three attempts at it before she got it so that it was free from mistakes, showed the jumble of her feelings. It was customary, she knew, to give some reason for leaving, but since Lawson had overlooked the courtesy of telling her she would soon be returning to statistics, she felt he could feel there was no discourtesy that she hadn't given him a reason for wanting to leave.

At five o'clock she hovered by her desk hoping Mrs Stavely would be in a hurry tonight. She didn't want her to see the tell-tale envelope she intended to leave on Lawson's blotter—she would see it in the morning, but she didn't want to go into an explanation with her tonight. But Mrs Stavely seemed to be in no hurry, and there was nothing for it but to put on her coat and go into the other room as she did every evening to say goodnight.

'Just off are you?' Mrs Stavely smiled when Ivory went in. 'I won't be far behind you. I just . . .' She stopped as she saw the envelope in Ivory's hand, then looked from her hand to her set face.

'I wanted Mr Alexander to have this when he comes in,' Ivory said, holding the envelope aloft. She met Mrs Stavely's eyes bravely, but found she couldn't smile.

Mrs Stavely wasn't smiling either as she said gently, 'If you're sure, my dear, then go and put it on his desk.'

CHAPTER TEN

IVORY went home with a feeling of that was that. She had set out this morning intending to do exactly what she had done. But whether she would have gone through with it if she hadn't been pushed into a corner, she couldn't have said. Lawson would find her resignation when he came in to-morrow, and what he would do when he read through it she had no idea. Probably nothing, she thought disconsolately, as she pushed her key into the lock and let herself into the flat, and she knew that would hurt more than anything if he just accepted her resignation without a word.

'Hello!' Mandy came bounding cheerfully out of the kitchen, and for all Ivory tried to give her a bright smile, Mandy stopped dead. 'You look as if you've lost five p. and found a penny—what's up?'

Mandy might as well know now as later. 'I've given in my notice,' she announced, and watched without really seeing as Mandy draped the tea towel she was carrying over the back of a chair and promptly dropped down on the arm.

'You don't sound very happy about it. What happened— or don't you want to tell?'

Ivory knew if she got started on the subject she would end up in floods of tears, though where they would all come from she couldn't think, for she felt she had wept her ten years' quota this last few days. 'Do you mind if . . .'

'Of course not,' Mandy said understandingly. 'Only please say you're hungry, because I've made an all-out effort tonight and cooked a sumptuous feast.'

Ivory was forced to laugh, for Mandy had many talents, but it was agreed between them that as a cook she was useless.

Over a meal of sausages, mash and peas, Mandy told Ivory she had planned to go out that night. 'I'm supposed to be meeting Adrian's boss and his wife, but I can't say I'm all that keen—I'll stay in with you if you like,' she offered.

'You'll do no such thing,' Ivory quickly rejected the offer, while thinking what a very good friend Mandy was. 'Adrian would have my scalp if you let him down and didn't go— with some justification too.'

'If you're sure,' Mandy hesitated.

'Of course I'm sure. I was a bit depressed when I came in, I admit—but your "sumptuous feast" soon put that right.'

They both laughed. 'Burnt sausages have a flavour all of their own,' Mandy opined, telling Ivory she could help herself to her peppermints if necessary, though she gave Ivory a worried look just before she went to answer Adrian's ring at the downstairs door. Then because she thought Ivory would be embarrassed if she pursued further the subject of her staying in, quipped, 'Old man Phillips must be working to rule—you'd have thought he would have answered the door by now.'

Left to herself when Mandy had gone, Ivory felt the first prickle of apprehension seep through her at the thought of facing Lawson tomorrow. As she had suspected it would, the fury that had been with her each time she thought of his careless treatment of her had cooled. He couldn't very well go through the whole month without once mentioning her impending departure—though in the light of what she knew of him, she wouldn't put anything past him.

Knowing she was in danger of going over the same ground for the umpteenth time and getting precisely nowhere, she banished all thoughts of Lawson and Alexander's, wishing fervantly that she'd never heard of the firm or its boss. Deciding to have a bath and then try to bury herself in a book until it was time to go to bed, Ivory left the sitting room with little hope that water gushing out from the bath taps would drown any encroaching thoughts about Lawson.

After her bath, she donned a fresh nightdress and pulling the belt of her thin tricel robe around her, brushed her honey-blonde hair back from her face. With a determination she hoped would take her through the evening, she took up the book she hoped would be so absorbing she wouldn't be able to put it down and made herself comfortable on the settee.

Footsteps on the landing outside alerted her to the fact that Mr Phillips was not working to rule after all as Mandy had suggested, and she waited for the knock she was sure was to come on the door of the flat.

Sure enough she heard the rapid tattoo sound on the wood panelling, and hoping it would be a flag-seller or someone with a charity appeal envelope so she could give them a donation and so be free of them, she went and opened the door.

Her first instinct when she saw Lawson Alexander standing there was to slam the door shut in his face—the way she was endeavouring to slam the door shut on the emotion she knew would tear her apart if she let it have its way.

'I thought you were in Oslo?' she said, resisting the impulse that would have made her seem unsophisticated and naïve in his eyes. For the look on his face, cold and remote, told her he had come to see her with some purpose in mind, and slamming the door in his face would not deter him from knocking until she opened the door again. 'You'd better come in,' she sighed in a resigned voice, and came away from the door.

He had not replied to her supposition that he was still in Oslo—a reply wasn't necessary anyway since he was standing in the middle of her carpet, Oslo many miles away. He had closed the door behind him, and the disturbed feeling he always managed to arouse in her fought with the control she was determined to exercise.

'When did you get back?' she asked, knowing the futility of asking him what he was doing calling at her flat—he would tell her when he was ready, not before. She indicated that he should take a seat, but when he sat at the opposite end of the settee from where she had been sitting—her book left open on the arm giving him ample evidence of that—she elected to seat herself in an easy chair furthest away from him. At that distance he was still suffocatingly close; any nearer and it would be unbearable.

His eyes flicked over her, and she thought he wasn't going to reply to her question, which had the tip of her tongue flicking out nervously to run over her lips. He seemed quite frightening sitting there, calmly looking at her. She wished he would say what he had come to say, then go. She was uncomfortably aware of her scanty attire, just thin nylon and tricel—even a touch of make-up would have given her some confidence, but her face was completely free of any artificial aids.

'I arrived back a short while ago,' he said at last, when Ivory thought she would soon start yelling if he didn't say something soon.

It came to her then that for some reason Lawson was intent on making her feel that way. He wanted her to lose her temper, wanted her saying things that normally wild horses wouldn't drag from her. She swallowed back her rising anger. Oh no—Lawson was a shrewd operator, but this time he wasn't going to call the tune. That being so, for all she would rather be fully dressed and with the maximum of make-up she allowed herself, she decided she would not react the way he was hoping for.

'May I get you a drink?' she asked pleasantly, rising to her feet in the manner of the perfect hostess for all the girdle of her robe was beginning to slip causing the top of her robe to gape open, exposing to the observant eye—and who was more observant than Lawson—an expanse of nylon and lace.

'Thank you,' Lawson accepted politely, when she was sure he would refuse. Though it did give her a chance to pull the slippery girdle more tightly about her when she had her back to him at the sideboard. Before she turned round she looked down at her front, and was horrified at the amount of nightdress that had been on view to his gaze. To put this to rights meant replacing the two glasses she had been about to carry over. But since she couldn't return to sit opposite him the way she was, she put the glasses down and adjusted her robe. Then picking up the glasses once more she went over to the settee and handed him the nip of Scotch that had been the last drop in the bottle—it had been there the six months she had been living with Mandy, so she hoped Scotch didn't go off—she knew very little about the spirit. Her own sherry she took with her and took a sip of it as she settled back down in her seat. She didn't want it, but it gave her something to do.

'How was Oslo?' she asked, trying to appear as though being in her night attire didn't bother her.

'Fine—what I saw of it,' Lawson answered smoothly, seeming to accept without any effort her attempts to play the well-mannered hostess.

'Oh . . .?' She thought she'd put just the right amount of enquiry into her voice.

'I didn't go to Norway just for the pleasure of it—beautiful country though it is. I went to meet a man over some business.'

She had no need to ask if his business was successful—for Lawson read success with a capital S, she thought, racking her brains to think of something bright to say next.

'Have you been busy today during my absence?' Lawson asked while she was still thinking.

She shrugged. 'You know what Mondays are like,' and then suddenly, alarm bells were jangling in her brain as the next thought struck her. 'You . . .' her voice came out all strangly and very much unlike the tone she had been adopting. She tried again—more slowly this time. 'Er—you haven't had time to go to the office?' she asked, then added without giving him time to answer, 'Of course you haven't, how silly of me, you wouldn't have had time if you haven't been back long.'

'Actually, I did have time.'

Her eyes flew to his, but she could make nothing of the cold expression that showed in his dark ones, though her heart was pounding loudly as it dawned on her he had received her resignation. And for all she had no idea why he should think it necessary to come and see her about it—that, she was now sure, was the reason for his visit.

'I would have thought we knew each other well enough for you to have waited until I came in tomorrow for you to tell me you wanted to leave,' Lawson went on, while she was still incapable of speech.

'I . . .' Really, he was the most maddening man, and what did he mean by 'knew each other well enough'? She hardly knew him at all. Yet wasn't that a lie—she knew so many things about him, he could be kind, courteous—arrogant when it suited him—Oh damn, she loved him, what else was there to know? She felt herself growing angry in spite of her good intentions. What right had he to make her feel guilty about not waiting until tomorrow—it was he who had withheld the information about Jenny's return. Stubbornly she refused to answer him. What was the point anyway—she knew from experience if there was to be a row, he was going to come out of it the victor.

'So you *don't* think you know me well enough to have waited?' he said, his voice changing, and she heard the crackle of ice that came with his next quesion. 'Perhaps, since you felt yourself unable to give me a reason for leaving in writing, you would care to give me that reason in person?'

Ooh, he was arrogant! How dare he use that tone on her when he was the guilty one! 'Surely you don't need me to tell you that?' she said shortly, and unable to sit still any longer, she left her chair.

Which was another mistake, she realised as soon as she had stood up, for Lawson too chose that moment to leave his seat, and as if someone had suddenly yelled 'Cut!' they faced each other across the carpet with about only a yard separating them. She couldn't understand the bleak look that came over his face briefly, but it had gone in an instant, and when he spoke again the coldness too had gone, and his voice was tight as if he was exerting a tremendous amount of will power over it.

'When's the wedding to be?' he asked abruptly.

'Wedding?' she queried, not at all with him, until she recalled telling him on the phone on Friday to mind his own business when he'd asked if she had accepted Jan's proposal. She wondered now how she'd dared to have the courage to tell him to mind his own business. But if he remembered what she'd said, it seemed he was more concerned with taking her to task for not stating her reasons in her letter for wanting to leave, rather than for her bad temper last Friday.

'When?' he repeated tersely. 'When are you getting married?'

'Why don't you ask Jan?' she said, playing for time, as the idea of telling him she was going to marry Jan crossed her mind.

If Lawson were to suspect later on that she was in love with him, he would discount that conclusion straight away if he thought she was going to marry Jan. Her mind raced on—but in the end, she was forced to reject the idea. Lawson was quite likely to contact Jan, might even congratulate him—their friendship demanded that even if he didn't think Jan was getting much of a bargain. But what about Jan's feelings if Lawson did that? No, she couldn't do it.

'I've been trying to contact Jan since Friday night,' Lawson told her. 'He was going to come in on this Norwegian deal, but he was nowhere around when things came to a head. But all that is beside the point . . .'

'I'm not going to marry Jan,' Ivory said quickly, as she knew she must.

'Not going to marry Jan?' Lawson repeated, as thought he wasn't hearing aright. 'I thought he asked you to marry him?'

'I don't have to marry every man who asks me!' she said hotly, then realising that sounded as if she had a proposal every day of her life, coloured, and said more slowly, 'I didn't mean that the way it sounded—I'm very fond of Jan, but—but I just don't love him.'

'So you wouldn't marry a millionaire unless you loved him?' Lawson asked slowly.

'I wouldn't marry any man unless I loved him,' she replied, some of the heat going out of her. Oh God, she was falling apart at the seams. She wished Lawson would go—any minute now he'd have her confessing it was him she loved, and she could just picture his embarrassment if she did that. She was more grateful than she could say that Lawson chose that moment to return to being his old arrogant self. At least when he was arrogant, she didn't feel so weak about him.

'Then if you aren't leaving to get married,' he demanded, his voice growing hard again, 'why the hell are you leaving?'

That did it. The pure unmitigated gall of the man! 'How dare you ask me that!' she flared. 'You know perfectly well I won't be working for you for much longer. You've known all the time that I was only replacing Jenny in a temporary capacity—you know full well you intend getting rid of me when she comes back.' She paused for breath, she knew her face was scarlet with temper, but far from it having the effect of making Lawson look uncomfortable, he seemed to be quite enjoying seeing the sparks flying from her eyes.

'Ah,' he said as if that explained everything. 'So you know, do you?'

'No thanks to you,' Ivory retorted rudely, and watched as his eyes narrowed at her tone. 'I . . . I was living in a little dream world all of my own, wasn't I,' she stammered, but refusing to apologise for her tone, '—enjoying the work I was doing—en-enjoying the responsibility. But I suppose when Jenny c-came back in a month or so's time, you'd have had me into your office—or p-perhaps not even that—but got Mrs Stavely to tell me m-my services were no longer required.'

'I would have seen you personally,' Lawson said evenly. 'But since Jenny isn't coming back for another four months, there would have been plenty of time to acquaint you with what was happening—and by that time . . .' He stopped, seeming to be at a loss for words, which was so out of character that Ivory stared at him.

'By that time—what?' she found herself prompting, and couldn't understand why the very air around her seemed to still as she waited for his answer.

'Before I tell you that,' he said slowly, his eyes seeming to search her face for something, 'I shall have to ask you in advance to forgive me.'

Ivory had no idea if he had found what he was looking for in her face, but his apologising in advance for whatever he was about to say or do in no way prepared her for the way he gathered her into his arms, and without haste gently laid his mouth against hers.

Her first instinct was to struggle, and briefly she had enough remaining reason to do just that. But her attempts to free herself were only half-hearted, as sheer surprise at finding herself in his arms took away most of her fight. Lawson didn't grip her tightly, but his hold on her was firm, and as his lips began to move against hers, so all the fight went out of her and she clung to him. His kiss deepened, and without the need of force, her lips parted, unaware of what she was doing. Her arms moved without her instruction and wound themselves around him. When he would have taken his mouth away from hers she was reluctant for him to do so, and as he stepped with her to the settee and she found herself being gently laid down upon it, she wanted the thrill of his love making to never end.

When he broke his kiss and sat up away from her, she could only stare at him with her heart in her eyes. She saw a smile break from him that turned into what could only be described as a grin of pure delight. His hands came down towards her and colour flared into her face as they hovered above her breasts, but the contact was only fleeting, and then only accidental when his hands gripped the edges of her robe that had worked loose and were gaping wide open. He pulled the edges of her robe together, thereby shutting out the picture of her delectable curves covered as they were only in filmy nylon.

'For my peace of mind, and what I have to say to you, I think it better that all temptation should be hidden from view,' he explained teasingly.

Ivory's face grew scarlet. She'd done it again, she realised, her emotions in tumultuous uproar. Once again she'd shown Lawson she was his for the asking. There was no way she was going to save her face now. She struggled to sit up, and Lawson, seeing her disquiet, lifted her until she was sitting beside him.

'I'm sorry I had to do that to you,' he apologised, though she couldn't help thinking he didn't sound very sorry—the reverse if anything. 'But everything is moving far more quickly than I intended and I had to have some answers—and fast.'

She already knew he wasn't a man to waste time, but this pronouncement that he wanted something to move more slowly—giving her no indication what—had her thoroughly bemused. And surely Lawson hadn't kissed her for the pure hell of it? 'I don't understand,' she said at last, finding herself unable to look at him, staring instead at a threadbare patch on the carpet. 'What is it that's moving too quickly for you?' Feeling his eyes burning into her, she just had to turn her head to look at him and saw he had a relenting expression on his face as he held her look.

'You have no idea?' he asked softly, and as she shook her head dumbly. 'In that case I'd better explain. I knew of course when Jenny left to have her baby that she'd be coming back to take up her old job . . .'

Ivory's lips tightened. 'You didn't think it important enough to mention it to me?'

'I thought about telling you, naturally,' he told her, 'but on reflection I decided against it.'

'But why?' She could see no good reason for him not to tell her, until the thought suddenly occurred to her. 'Was it because you thought I might not accept the job in the first place if I'd known it was only temporary?'

'That thought did cross my mind, I must admit—and I'll admit also that I was determined to have you working for me.'

'Were you?' she asked, her eyes growing wide. 'I know I'm fairly good at my job, but I'm sure you employ other secretaries who are up to my speeds and probably faster.'

'Agreed,' said Lawson, which slightly dampened the glow she was starting to feel that he thought so well of her work he was determined to have her work for him. 'But none of the other secretaries have a certain shade of honey-blonde hair or violet blue eyes that interfere with my normal thought processes.'

At his words Ivory jerked round so that she was facing him. What was he saying? That she'd got the job not because of her shorthand and typing speeds, but because . . . 'You engaged me just because of the colour of my hair and eyes?' she gasped disbelievingly.

'Not only that,' he said seriously. 'I admired your beauty from the moment I first saw you—all tousle-haired with your cheeks flushed like a child's fresh from sleep

Ivory's mind went back to her first meeting with him when she had woken up in his bedroom, and she flushed uncomfortably. Lawson smiled at her and she had the strangest impression that he wanted to take her in his arms again, nothing would allow her to let him, she thought firmly. But what was he saying about her interfering with his normal thought processes? Before she could even begin to unravel the mystery of that remark, Lawson seemed to make an effort to get back to what he was saying.

'It's not only your physical attributes I admire, Ivory,' he went on, to her growing amazement. 'From the beginning I've been forced to acknowledge qualities in you I'd begun to think had gone out of fashion—in Amsterdam when I unthinkingly thought I'd help you out of the predicament you found yourself in by paying for a new dress, you left me in no doubt of the pride in you and what you thought about my offer. I soon realised too, that in an age where sleeping around seems to be an acceptable part of every day living, you stand out for your high moral principles.'

He was making her sound something she was not, Ivory thought. She had pride, certainly, but the high moral principles he was talking of were non-existent when she was in his arms—surely he must realise that—yet, unbelievably, it seemed he hadn't. And more unbelievably, he was no longer the arrogant, aggressive man she had thought him to be when he had entered her flat earlier. He seemed to have changed completely, and far from giving her a bad time because she had given in her notice, he was now quietly telling her of the qualities he liked about her. Her heart was beating so loudly within her, she was sure he would soon hear it.

'So you wanted me to work for you be-because you—er —like—er—certain things about me,' she said hesitantly, her throat suddenly gone dry.

'I wanted you working with me because I wanted to get to know you better,' Lawson said quietly, his voice so serious falling into the echoing silence of the room. 'And,' he added slowly, as if he wanted more than every word he was saying to get through, 'I wanted you to get to know me.'

'I . . . I . . . Why?' It was no good her trying to sort out for herself why Lawson should think it so important they got to know each other, her mental processes were shooting off in all directions, and the one thing she knew she wanted him to mean, she just knew could not be what he meant.

'Why,' he answered quite simply. 'Because I love you, and . . .'

'You love me!' Ivory exclaimed, her eyes filling with tears at the shock his words gave her. 'You can't,' she said disbelievingly. Then huskily, because he was being too cruel to play with her like this when he must now have guessed how she felt about him, 'You don't mean it, do you?'

For answer he made the first physical contact since he had lifted her to a sitting position after his kiss had sent her senses scattering. His arm came about her, and he pulled her against his shoulder so he could see into her face. She felt his body heat warm against hers and began trembling as she waited for his reply.

'My beautiful darling,' he told her gently, the trembling of her body reaching him through her thin covering, 'I lost my head and my heart to you in Amsterdam.'

'Oh, Lawson!' Ivory murmured as her tears spilled over.

It was all she could manage, but it seemed to be enough for him for the moment, as with gentle fingers he wiped her tears away. Then she was in his arms and as his mouth came down over hers she could feel the vibrant throbbing of his heart against hers as each hurried beat sounded time with the other.

When at last he put her away from him, he looked deep

into her eyes. 'Should I take it from your response just now that you love me too?' he asked, and though she knew he couldn't be in any doubt, he seemed to be holding himself stiffly until he had her answer.

'You must know I love you,' she told him shyly, and felt the thrill of his arms tightening around her, a look of relief on his face so great she only then began to realise how much he really loved her and how anxiously he had been waiting for her answer.

It was wonderful just being in Lawson's arms. Ivory had thought there was no further need for words, but was thrilled by the endearments he showered on her then—the way he kissed her between sentences as if too much time had been spent on other things when they should have been in each other's arms.

When the arm about her relaxed, she was quite content, but looking at him saw a rueful look come over his face. 'You're a very heady woman, Miss Dutton—do you know that?' and not waiting for her answer, for all her eyes twinkled delightfully at his compliment, 'I really think I'd better stop kissing you for a while—I fear my will power at the moment is not equal to yours.'

Ivory could only stare at him. Didn't he know that where he was concerned, she had no will power at all? Then Lawson proved he had will power in full measure, for when she enquired into his reason for not telling her Jenny was coming back, he set her away from him, and seemed ready to clear up anything that was worrying her.

'I fell in love with you, my love, when we were in Holland. To be truthful, I wasn't very happy about it. I suppose you could say it was an emotion I distrusted—I'm thirty-five and have used up a lot of living in those thirty-five years. Without meaning to be unkind to the Shebas and Louises of this world, forever with their eye to the main chance, they do tend to give one a jaundiced view of the female species.'

Imperceptibly Ivory relaxed. Both Louise and Sheba were beautiful women, but at Lawson's words, she knew she had no need to be jealous of them or any other woman who might set her cap at him.

'To get back to what I was saying, there I was expecting Dizzy and you turn up with violet eyes flashing, and I know I'm sinking fast. I told myself it wasn't happening—that I wouldn't let it happen, yet before I knew it I'd made up my mind you were going to have dinner with me. When you walked out on me afterwards with such indecent haste, not even waiting to finish your coffee, I was furious. I was determined you wouldn't walk out on me again, and I made you come with me to the dinner I'd arranged with Jan.' Ivory remembered she had been under the threat of dismissal if she hadn't done as he asked, but refrained from mentioning this as he continued, 'I wasn't prepared to admit to myself that I wanted to show off to him the woman I'd fallen in love with, for all he's a very great friend.'

'What about Jan?' Ivory asked, suddenly seeing Jan's face as she had seen it the last time.

'I didn't count on Jan falling in love with you,' Lawson admitted, his face serious for a moment. 'Don't you worry about it, sweetheart,' he said, seeing the worried look on her face. 'I'll contact Jan—I think he's big enough to take it on the chin, for all he'll hate my guts for a while.'

'Will he?' she questioned, not wanting to be the one to come between two such great friends.

'I was prepared to hate him when I thought he'd snatched you from under my nose,' Lawson admitted, his look telling her he wasn't joking.

Ivory leaned towards him and kissed away the dark look

from his brow. She thought he was going to take her in his arms once more and felt the tightening pressure on her arms before he set her away from him.

'I said you were a heady female,' he told her, a smile on his face once more. 'I'm afraid if you provoke me too much I shan't be responsible for my actions.' He gave her the wickedest grin so far, which told her what he meant.

'I fought against loving you, Ivory,' he admitted. 'But I might just as well have saved myself the torment, for when you turned up with Jan at the Fenwick, I knew the battle I'd been fighting since our return from Holland was lost.'

Ivory was amazed that Lawson had loved her all that time, and she couldn't help but tell him he had never shown he was attracted to her until they had been in Manchester, and then she had thought it had been the desire of the moment.

'I knew you weren't remotely interested in me,' he told her. 'I thought you disliked me—and that I thought was some reaction at least. I'd been looking for a replacement for Jenny. You sprang to mind dozens of times, but as I said, you spelt danger, so I looked in other directions. Then after seeing you at the Fenwick I decided it had to be you. Oh, not specifically to do the work, even though I knew you were up to it.'

'Why, then?' Ivory put in, knowing that, good at her job as Lawson thought she was, she was nowhere equal to sorting out the intricacies of his mind.

'I knew you'd had a love affair that had gone sour,' he told her, his face hardening briefly as thoughts of her ex-fiancé intruded. 'You'd told me he meant nothing to you and I wanted to believe it—but I couldn't. I was as jealous as hell of the swine. Anyway, I knew Jenny wouldn't be back for some five or six months and I'd hoped that during that time you might come to care for me a little.'

'Oh Lawson!' Ivory breathed. He would never know how much she loved him, though she would do her best to show him. 'But,' she exclaimed, as she recalled the very unlover-like way he had behaved with her, 'you never showed in any way that you thought of me as anything but someone to sharpen your temper on.'

'Was I that bad?' Lawson enquired, smiling. 'I must admit we do tend to strike sparks off each other, though I will say in my defence that I'd planned to woo you slowly. I wasn't sure, as I said, whether you were still pining for your ex-fiancé, so I didn't want to put you off by showing you how I felt straight away. If Mrs Stavely hadn't let it out about Jenny, I intended trying a gradual breakdown process over the next four months. Seeing your resignation on my desk when I went into the office tonight made me realise I had no time to woo you—I was as nervous as hell when I knocked on your door tonight,' he confessed. 'God knows what I would have done if you'd confirmed my worst suspicion and said you were leaving to get married.'

Ivory could hear the desolation in his voice as he relived his feelings of that moment, and snuggled against him as if to assure him she was his completely.

'I thought you must have guessed my feelings,' she told him, 'when I reacted to your kisses the way I did in Manchester.'

'You knew you loved me then?' Lawson questioned.

'I'd discovered it the night before,' she confessed. 'I was terrified in case you guessed.'

'And I thought I'd half frightened you to death when I let you see I wanted you,' he said. 'I love you so much, my darling.'

Ivory smiled in deep contentment. Lawson loved her as she loved him—unbelievably, he wanted her; out of all the other more clever more sophisticated women he knew, he wanted *her*. And what was more, he made her feel she had no need to be jealous of them. Her feelings all for him, she recalled that he had said he had been jealous of Michael, and since she didn't want to have any doubts between them, she told him:

'I thought I was in love once before,' looking into his eyes, and seeing a slight withdrawal that told her since they were clearing away every obstacle, it had been right for her to bring the subject up. 'But it was never like this.'

'Wasn't it?' His voice seemed detached suddenly.

'No, darling, it wasn't,' she said softly. 'Michael and I broke up because I couldn't do what he asked—I know now that I never really loved him.'

'How?'

Just the one word, but there was agression creeping in, and she couldn't help feeling panicky that she might be losing Lawson before whatever relationship he had in mind had even began.

'B-Because,' she began, her face going pink as he held her eyes, 'Because I love you so much—you wouldn't need to ask.'

Immediately the cold look left Lawson's face to be replaced by an adoring look she had never thought to witness. 'Oh, my darling, darling Ivory,' he said, taking her into his arms. 'God give me strength that I can hold out until after our wedding!'

JOY

ROMANCE

LOVE

Harlequin Omnibus

THREE love stories in ONE beautiful volume

The joys of being in love...
the wonder of romance...
the happiness that true love brings...

Now yours in the HARLEQUIN OMNIBUS
edition every month wherever
paperbacks are sold.

Harlequin Presents...

The beauty of true romance...

The excitement of world travel...

The splendor of first love...

NEW FROM HARLEQUIN

YOUR 1980 ROMANCE HOROSCOPE!

Harlequin Reader Service

In U.S.A.
M.P.O. Box 707
Niagara Falls, NY 14302

In Canada
649 Ontario Street
Stratford, Ontario, N5A 6W2

Please send me the following Harlequin Romance Horoscope volumes. I am enclosing a check or money order of $1.75 for each volume ordered, plus 40¢ to cover postage and handling.

☐ **Aries**
(Mar. 21-Apr. 20)

☐ **Taurus**
(Apr 21-May 22)

☐ **Gemini**
(May 23-June 21)

☐ **Cancer**
(June 22-July 22)

☐ **Leo**
(July 23-Aug. 22)

☐ **Virgo**
(Aug. 23-Sept. 22)

☐ **Libra**
(Sept. 23-Oct. 22)

☐ **Scorpio**
(Oct. 23-Nov. 21)

☐ **Sagittarius**
(Nov. 22-Dec. 22)

☐ **Capricorn**
(Dec. 23-Jan. 20)

☐ **Aquarius**
(Jan. 21-Feb. 19)

☐ **Pisces**
(Feb. 20-Mar. 20)

Number of volumes checked @ $1.75 each $_____

N.Y. and N.J. residents add appropriate sales tax $_____

Postage and handling $_____.40

TOTAL: $_____

I am enclosing a grand total of $_____

NAME_____

ADDRESS_____

STATE/PROV._____ ZIP/POSTAL CODE_____

ROM 2297